How to Grow Psilocybin Mushrooms at Home for Beginners

5 Comprehensive Magic Mushroom Growing Methods & All You Need to Know About Psilocybin

Inspirational Creator

from various sources. Please consult a licensed professional before attempting any techniques outlined in this book.

By reading this document, the reader agrees that under no circumstances is the author responsible for any losses, direct or indirect, that are incurred as a result of the use of the information contained within this document, including, but not limited to, errors, omissions, or inaccuracies.

ISBN 978-1-922940-117 (E-book)
ISBN 978-1-922940-124 (Paperback)

Cover Design by Bil Harret
Published by Inspirational Creator
Bil Harret & Anastasia V. Sasha
First Edition (2023)

Table of Contents

Disclaimer: This book has been written mainly for educational and informative purposes. You will be using this book and the information that it contains at your own discretion. Please note that Psilocybin is an illegal substance and I do not condone or encourage its use or cultivation in parts of the world where it is against the law to do so. I do, however, realize that illegal drug use will occur, and I believe that responsible and educational information is crucial to keep users safe. Please consult your medical provider if you are under any form of medical treatment.

Introduction

For the adventurous mushroom forager, there is no better feeling than coming across a crop of psilocybin—*magic*—mushrooms in the wild. These little fruiting patches represent a mere fraction of the vast subterranean network of fungi. It is a wonderfully fascinating and near-perfect system, nurtured by the very best of cultivators: Mother Nature herself. Foraging for mushrooms is a great way to immerse yourself in nature and can be a hugely rewarding pastime. However, it requires specialist knowledge and a lot of time and patience. Furthermore, with an estimated 1.5 million species in the fungi kingdom—and 90% of those yet to be discovered—there are many poisonous and deadly lookalikes out there that can pose a threat to the inexperienced. So if you are a beginner, trust me when I tell you that growing your own magic mushrooms is easier than picking them in the wild. As well as the benefits of safety, home cultivation is relatively straightforward and cheap, and it yields far greater harvests. The best part? Anyone can do it!

But first, let's have a brief look at the history of fungi. About 450 million years ago, fungi formed a symbiosis with the plants that lived in the primordial ocean. With their mycelium, they assumed the function of a root system and thus made it possible for aquatic plants to establish themselves on land with their rudimentary roots. Without fungi, neither trees nor plants would have developed. This in turn caused land animals to evolve, which eventually supported the survival and progress of early humans.

The influence of fungi on human civilization began in ancient times. It is known that mushrooms containing psilocybin were ingested by our ancestors, but an incredible discovery in Algeria revealed just how far back the fungi-human relationship stretched. In the caves of Tassili n'Ajjer, late Neolithic rock art portrays what looks like a bee-headed shaman with little mushrooms sprouting from his body. He is accompanied by a group of people who are holding mushrooms and appear to be affected by their hallucinogenic qualities. Dated to around 4700 BC, the rock art is the earliest evidence of psilocybin mushrooms being used ritually. The peoples of Mesoamerica, Europe, and Siberia also have a long-standing history of ingesting magic mushrooms for spiritual and medicinal purposes.

It has been theorized that psilocybin mushrooms have had a profound impact on the evolution of humans. While there are several different versions of how mankind evolved from apes to homo sapiens, a striking theory is that of the "Stoned Ape," presented by Terence Mckenna in 1992. It explains how psilocybin mushrooms could have been the catalyst for homo erectus evolving into homo sapiens. These early humans had domesticated cattle by this point, and psilocybin species had begun to thrive in the animal dung. Mckenna suggests that our ancestors ate these mushrooms, which in turn created and enhanced neural pathways in their brains. As a result, they moved away from their primal way of thinking and developed a new self-consciousness, a new perception of time, and the ability to process information on a much higher level.

Mckenna's theory proposes that magic mushrooms are the "missing link" that people have searched for—that one piece in the evolutionary puzzle that can explain why two million years ago the brain exploded and the human cortex tripled in size within a comparably short period of time. While it has not been strictly proven, it is certain that this extraordinary species can have a powerful effect on the brain. American psychologist Timothy Leary said that in the course of a few hours after taking mushrooms containing psilocybin, he learned more about the mind than he had in his entire career of over fifteen years! Research into psilocybin that started in the 1970s but was halted by authorities is now starting to pick up again, and already the results are striking. Several scientific studies have shown that psilocybin mushrooms have a profoundly positive effect on people suffering from OCD, PTSD, cluster headaches, depression, addiction, and more. They have also demonstrated extraordinary therapeutic qualities for patients with cancer and terminal illnesses. I will cover the effects psilocybin has on the brain in more detail in the final chapter.

One thing is clear: fungi are the underrated superheroes of this world, and humanity has already benefited hugely from them. They are the facilitators of all life forms.

They regenerate the environment, help save diseased trees and increase crop yield, provide us with powerful nutrition and medicines, and break down pollutants in the atmosphere. They can even absorb heavy metals from contaminated farmland and, in some cases, neutralize radioactive radiation in the ground, not to mention the fact that they taste delicious! I believe that fungi and their mycelium networks could play an essential role in the future. We could use them to restore our planet's biodiversity, leading to green deserts instead of the barren, sandy ones that are currently predicted. They could form the building blocks for houses, being resilient and energy-efficient, not to mention cheap and sustainable. Who knows! They might even help solve the crisis of food and energy resources. We are only scratching the surface of the many ways fungi can help save our planet.

This book will go through the main techniques—*teks*—for growing psilocybin mushrooms at home: PF Tek, Uncle Ben's Tek, Monotub Tek, Martha Tent Tek, and outdoor cultivation. Some are slightly more lengthy than others and require more equipment. This is why I will cover a variety of teks so that you can compare them and figure out which works best for you. I will focus on the *Psilocybe cubensis* species (genus Psilocybe) as they are the most common, suitable, and widely accessible psychedelic mushrooms. One of the most common complaints beginners have when they look into home cultivation is the sheer amount of information out there, which is often contradictory and overwhelmingly technical. This book will aim to keep it super simple and gather the most useful information in one place. It is my hope that, after reading this, you will feel confident about growing psilocybin mushrooms at home. You will have a range of methods to choose from and refer to, and you will be well-versed in the ideologies and benefits behind home cultivation!

Chapter 1: The Fungi Life Cycle

The fungi life cycle is simple. Germination is triggered when two microscopic spores meet in an environment with favorable growing conditions. *Psilocybe cubensis* spores can thrive in a number of different organic matters, although cow dung is their particular favorite. In each case, the growth medium must be moist, nutrient-rich, not too cold, and not directly exposed to sunlight. Once the spores have germinated, they begin producing mycelium, the fungi's root-like system of delicate white threads called hyphae. The mycelium then spreads through the growth medium in search of food and water. This process is called colonization. It is a crucial step in the fungi life cycle as, unlike plants, fungi do not contain chlorophyll and therefore cannot photosynthesize in order to get food. They rely on oxygen and nutrients to survive and release carbon dioxide as a waste product. In this sense, they are closer to animals than other plant life.

Once the mycelium has fully colonized the growth medium and can go no further, it produces fruiting bodies, or, as we know them, mushrooms. The mushrooms grow towards the direction of light (typically upwards), which explains why many cultivators keep the lower part of their fruiting chamber dark to avoid side pinning. As mushrooms mature, they tend to flatten and eventually open their gills, releasing their spores into the air. These spores are then carried by the breeze to the next pile, where the process begins all over again.

Fun fact: Trees and other plants take advantage of the sophisticated mycelial network to transport their own nutrients through the ground. A mother tree feeds its surrounding seedlings, for example. They can also use the system to send warning signals. For instance, if a tree is attacked by aphids or pathogens, it will use the underground mycelial channels to alert other trees in the area, which in turn will produce defense chemicals and distribute them. Trees and plants also use the mycelial network to communicate about water availability in the soil. This is why it is sometimes referred to as the Wood Wide Web: nature's very own internet fiber optic cables!

Optimal Growing Conditions: Mimicking Nature

Now that you understand the life cycle of fungi, you will have a better idea of the process you are trying to replicate indoors. Essentially, you are aiming to re-create the conditions in which mushrooms are happiest in the wild. The key to optimal growing conditions is to monitor these four factors: temperature, air exchange, moisture, and light exposure.

- **Temperature**: The average indoor temperature should be fine for growing mushrooms. However, it is advisable to keep the temperature between 25-28°C (77-82°F) when the mycelium is growing. Once the pinning process begins (typically induced with a cold shock for cold weather species), adjust the temperature to about 22-24°C (71-75°F) to allow for maximum growth. To clarify, a temperature drop is not needed to trigger the pinning process for *Psilocybe cubensis* (a tropical species), but lowering the fruiting temperature will allow for better results. Most mushrooms need some sort of temperature drop to fruit successfully.

- **Air exchange**: Up until the pinning stage, the substrate needs very little air exchange. As pins start to appear, more oxygen should be introduced. This is to prevent mold growth and a build-up of CO_2 levels, which would stall the mycelium. More air exchange also causes the evaporation of moisture, which is the main pinning trigger.

- **Moisture**: The substrate should be moist enough that you could squeeze a couple of drops of water out of it. This is called being at "field capacity." If it is too dry or too wet the mycelium will not thrive, plus too much moisture is the perfect breeding ground for contaminants like mold. While the mycelium is colonizing the grain the humidity should be high, at 95-100%. Once the pinning stage has begun, the humidity should be reduced to 90-95% and the sides of the growing tub or bag should be misted with water several times a day.

- **Light exposure**: While the mycelium is colonizing the grain, very little light is needed. However, as pinning occurs, light exposure is important as it directs the mushrooms to grow upwards. A room with natural or dappled light is ideal, or some growers prefer to use artificial lighting. Do not place the substrate in direct sunlight as this will harm the mycelium.

If you get all of these factors right and sterilize your equipment and workspace sufficiently, you can't go wrong!

Stages of Cultivation

While the growing techniques may vary slightly, the stages of cultivation are essentially the same each time. How long your mushrooms take to grow depends on the spores you get and how well you set up your growing conditions. Generally, though, the whole process should take between 6–12 weeks.

- **Strain Selection**: Select which strain of mushroom you want to cultivate and purchase the spores accordingly.

See **Chapter 2: Selecting a Candidate for Cultivation** for my recommendations on which strains to pick.

- **Preparation**: Fully prepare and sterilize your room, equipment, and yourself. This includes preparing and sterilizing an adequate substrate so that it is free of contaminants and retains the right moisture. I will bang on about this *a lot*. See **Chapter 2: Contamination Factors and Best Practices** for an in-depth explanation of how to sufficiently sterilize your workspace.

- **Inoculation**: Using a spore syringe, or any other inoculum, introduce your spores or mycelium culture to the grain medium. Try to distribute the spores evenly as this will speed up the incubation.

- **Incubation (2–4 weeks)**: This refers to the time it takes for the mycelium to fully colonize the substrate once it has been inoculated. The spores merge into the substrate and mycelium starts to spread outwards from the inoculation points. This stage of the process is particularly susceptible to contamination as the mycelium has not yet established a firm hold over the substrate.

- **Colonization (in parallel with incubation, 2–4 weeks)**: This process occurs during the incubation period. The mycelium continues to cover the substrate, seeking water and nutrients to multiply itself and consolidate its hold.

- **Consolidation (1 week)**: After the substrate has been fully colonized, let it sit for a week to allow the mycelium to strengthen itself.

- **Pinning (1–2 weeks)**: Primordia, or "pins," start to appear. These will mature into mushrooms.

- **Fruiting (1–2 weeks)**: Mushrooms start to grow. This is the most exciting bit!

- **Harvesting**: Your mushrooms are ready for picking when the caps are conical-shaped and the veil underneath looks like it's about to break and flatten out. Cut them at the base, close to the substrate. Make sure you harvest the mushrooms before they fully mature as they start to lose their potency after that.

- **Flush and Repeat**: A "flush" refers to a crop of mushrooms that have grown at the same time. Once you have harvested your mushrooms and received your first "flush," the substrate can usually produce two or three additional flushes! Simply rinse it in water and repeat the process from the pinning stage. The best part about this is second flushes tend to give larger yields than the first!

The mycelium will continue to produce mushrooms until all of the available water and nutrients in the substrate have been exhausted. You will know when this happens. Contaminants may also start to grow. At this point, you should dispose of the substrate in a secure bag outside.

Chapter 2: Key Factors for Growing

Contamination Factors and Best Practices

By far the biggest obstacle for home growers is contamination. As a general rule of thumb, contaminating organisms grow faster than mushroom mycelium. Thus, it only takes one contaminant getting into your substrate to destroy the whole process. In order to avoid contamination, you must follow a rigorous procedure for sterilization. This includes cleaning and sterilizing all of your equipment in between each step of the growing process. The bottom line: the more sterilization, the better. If it feels excessive, you're probably getting it just right. Don't worry, though; I will list all of the equipment you'll need at the beginning of each growing method.

It is useful to think of contamination as coming from six potential areas. Here I follow Paul Stamets' (2000) categorization of "the vectors of contamination."

The Cultivator: This means you! Imagine that your body is a haven for microorganisms. The most common way to spread bacteria and viruses is through breath or touch. This is why it's important to wear laboratory gloves and a face mask when working with fungi. If you don't like wearing gloves, washing your hands with antibacterial soap every 20 minutes should suffice. Falling skin flakes can also pose problems, so make sure you have a shower and put on clean clothes before handling any growing equipment.

The Air: Paul Stamets describes the air as a "sea of microorganisms hosting invisible contaminants." Try and avoid growing your mushrooms in a room that opens directly onto the outside world, as this will greatly increase the risk of contaminants getting in each time you enter the room. You can disinfect the room using commercial sprays like Lysol. Spray the mist as close to the ceiling as possible while walking backwards towards the door. Leave the room for a minute or two before re-entering. Ensure the room is clean, but do not vacuum before handling the growing equipment, as this can stir up contaminants in the air.

The Media: The most common cause of contamination is the growing medium not being sufficiently sterilized. Your substrate is most vulnerable to contaminants during the inoculation and incubation stages, before the mycelium consolidates its hold on the substrate. Once the grains have been fully colonized, they are protected by the mycelium, and you're pretty much in the clear. Traditionally, substrates have been sterilized in pressure cookers. This is not the most straightforward process, as you will see in the PF Tek. If it's your first time growing mushrooms, I would therefore recommend buying an already sterilized growing medium or using techniques that don't require this step, such as Uncle Ben's.

The Tools: Sterilizing your tools each step of the way is essential. The best way is to use a combined method of flame sterilization followed by alcohol disinfection. A butane or propane torch lighter can be used to sterilize your syringe needle, and 70% Isopropyl rubbing alcohol can then be used to wipe down the whole syringe and any other equipment you may be using. If you are using a pressure cooker, remember to sterilize the outside as well; just because the interior is sterile doesn't mean contaminants can't be picked up from hands touching the exterior.

The Inoculum: This refers to the mushroom tissue that is being transferred from one place to another, such as spores or parts of the mycelium. Every time you transfer the inoculum, you are exposing it to bacteria. Refer to the above points on how to take steps towards safely isolating and moving the inoculum.

Mobile Contamination Units (MCUs): MCUs can range from tiny organisms such as flies, ants, and mites to household pets and other humans. Obviously, the smaller the organism, the harder it is to control. Mites are particularly difficult due to their microscopic size and fondness for eating fungi. Should you experience a mite infestation, your only hope is to remove everything, cleanse the room with bleach three times, and start again. But let's hope it doesn't come to that. Some mushroom cultivators have reported using "decontamination mats" under and around their growing stations. Professional laboratories use these at the entrances to doors, and they can prove very effective for preventing meddling MCUs from entering your workspace.

With all these contamination factors, the important thing to remember is to keep exposure time to a minimum. The longer your mycelium is exposed to contamination, the more severe the consequences will be. If you notice any signs of contamination, especially in the early stages of cultivation where it can expand faster, remember that time is of the essence. If you deal with it quickly and carefully, it may not be a lost cause. Furthermore, be sure to source your spores from a reputable supplier. Many cases of contamination are due to faulty spore syringes. See the heading **Sourcing Your Spores and Other Supplies** in this chapter for more information.

Pasteurization vs Sterilization

Pasteurizing or sterilizing your substrate is extremely important. This eliminates any contaminants that may be growing in the organic material. But what's the difference between the two?

Pasteurization: This process occurs when you heat your substrate up to 65-85°C (149-185°F) using either hot water or steam. Let it pasteurize for two hours. This will kill most of the harmful microorganisms, but not all.

Sterilization: This follows a similar process but requires a much higher temperature, about 120°C or more (248°F plus). You will most likely need a pressure cooker to reach these higher temperatures. Sterilization kills all other microorganisms living in your substrate.

Which method to use depends on the material you are using. For example, if you have opted for straw, pasteurization will suffice, as straw has a relatively low level of nutrients. Sometimes it is even advantageous to pasteurize instead of sterilize, as not all microorganisms are threatening and can benefit the mycelium if they remain in the substrate. If you are using a nutrient-rich material such as hardwood, sterilization is recommended, as the high level of nutrients means there is a higher risk of competing microorganisms that are harmful to the mycelium.

Sourcing your Spores and Other Supplies

If you are a first-time grower and a little nervous about sourcing your psilocybin spores, let me reassure you. There are ways to acquire them that don't legally implicate you. The spores themselves are simply single cells used by fungi to reproduce. They don't contain the controlled substances psilocybin or psilocin. The sale of spores for the purposes of microscopy and other scientific research is therefore perfectly legitimate. I'm afraid the states of California, Georgia, and Idaho are exceptions to this. If you find yourself in one of these three unlucky states, you should consider ordering your spores from a different state.

There are several reputable suppliers online that will ship spores and growing kits. A good way to check whether they are safe or not is to check if they match the following criteria: Does the website look legitimate? Does it have an *About Us* page with contact details? Do they mention quality control methods? Check to see if the supplier is well-reviewed. Consult online forums and social media platforms for reviews and customer feedback. Do not order spores directly from sites like Instagram or Facebook.

Remember, you can always ask questions! If the supplier is legitimate, they will have an easily contactable customer service team. What procedures are in place for maintaining sterile lab conditions? How fresh are their spores, and how do they prepare their syringes? Do they offer refunds/replacements for faulty spore syringes or damaged growing kits? Vendors are unlikely to answer any direct questions about growing magic mushrooms due to the legal implications, so try to keep questions about the spores themselves. If they are slow to respond or give vague, non-committal answers, stay on the safe side and look for another supplier.

Syringes containing *Psilocybe cubensis* spores cost about $20 online and can usually be stored for up to 6 months before use. There are many organizations that will scam you online, and, because of the legal grey area, once you have purchased your spores, you are no longer protected from fraud. Foraging for your own spores is also an option, but we will cover this in more depth in **Chapter 9: How to Collect Spores**.

Once you have ordered your spores, sourcing the rest of the supplies is much more straightforward. All of the growing equipment listed in this book can be found in local supermarkets and hardware stores or bought online.

Selecting a Candidate for Cultivation

Psilocybe cubensis is the most widely cultivated species of magic mushroom in the world. It is no surprise, then, that there are hundreds of different strains out there to choose from. This is something that can overwhelm beginners when they first start looking into selecting a candidate for home cultivation. Please don't worry too much. There is a saying amongst psychonauts that "a cube is a cube," and it's true that you're not going to get wildly different results from taking different strains of *P. cubensis*, especially if you're micro-dosing. Nevertheless, I would recommend Golden Teacher or B+ for beginners, as they are wonderfully resistant to contamination and will grow even in unfavorable conditions. Amazonians are known for their rapid colonization and large yields. These three strains are arguably the most common and are readily available online. Cambodian and Penis Envy may not be available on all sites but are nevertheless widely accessible. They are known for having a higher potency than most other *P. cubensis* strains.

Chapter 3: Growing Kit vs Your Own Hardware

As we have seen in the previous chapter, the great thing about growing mushrooms at home is that you can source all of the supplies yourself and for relatively little money. If it's all sounding a bit complicated still, there is an even easier option: purchasing a ready-made growing kit. Many beginners prefer to do this as it skips the tedium of having to prepare the substrate and sterilize everything. It also means you don't have to source your spores separately. Please remember, there is no shame in opting for this method. It is still a great introduction to home cultivation, and once you've experienced your first successful flush, you may have the confidence to try it from scratch next time! Just remember to take the same precautions as when sourcing your spores online, as outlined in the previous chapter.

Some websites make the good point that if you have purchased a growing kit online, you can leave it for a week after it arrives before inoculating. This way, you will be able to see if any contamination entered the bag during transit. I know that some sites offer replacements for bags that arrive damaged. Consult your chosen organization's website for its specific policies on this.

Grain Medium, Bulk Substrate, and Casing Layer

You may be thinking—What's the difference between a grain medium and a bulk substrate? The grain medium is what you inoculate with psilocybin spores in order to grow mycelium. You then add this to the bulk substrate, which provides a structure for the fully colonized grain medium to fruit in. It's the same as buying a plant in a shop and then transferring it to a larger pot full of nice, rich soil at home.

Getting the bulk substrate right is important. Fungi are a little pickier than plants; you can't just pop to the store and buy any old bag of soil. They need an organic material full of juicy, decaying matter. Bear in mind that you also want to pick a substrate that's easy for you to work with. The most common materials are hardwood sawdust, straw, coco coir, and vermiculite. Personally, I would recommend a mixture of coco coir and vermiculite. Not only are these materials readily available in gardening centers or horticultural stores, but they are also a personal favorite of *Psilocybe cubensis* to grow in. The coco coir and vermiculite mix should be pasteurized before coming into contact with the mycelium.

Sawdust and straw are also favored by home growers, especially as they are waste products from places like construction sites and agricultural farms. This makes them cheap and easy to get a hold of. But remember, if you are going to use sawdust, it must be from hardwood trees such as ash, maple, or oak. Our species of mushroom does not like softwood. Of course, if you *really* wanted to mimic natural growing conditions, you could use manure. However, to be used as a substrate, manure needs to be mixed with straw and undergo multiple pasteurizations. For this reason, it is not widely used by beginners.

It is a similar story with the grain medium; the one you choose is up to you. Some common grains are brown rice, birdseed, or rye berries. The latter is a favorite amongst mushroom cultivators. All work well with *Psilocybe cubensis*. The most important thing is that your grain medium is hydrated, nutrient-rich, and clean, as this is what your mycelium is going to colonize. You can buy these grains at most supermarkets or organic food shops. The casing layer is the material used to act as a barrier between the colonized grain medium and any airborne contaminants. Coco coir, vermiculite, or a mixture of both are very effective, and they also help to retain moisture.

Chapter 4: PF Tek Method

The PF Tek is one of the oldest growing techniques. Developed by Robert "Psilocybe Fanaticus" McPherson, it introduced a game-changer to home cultivation: adding vermiculite to the grain medium. You will see why this matters once you start growing! Despite being an oldie, this method is still widely used because it is cheap and easy to do.

What you need:

Equipment:

- 10 ½ pint wide mouth mason jars (BALL or KERR are the best)

- mixing bowl

- measuring cups

- strainer

- pressure cooker*

- aluminum foil

- metal rack

- mist spray bottle

- micropore tape

- clear plastic box, min. 50L

- electric drill + quarter-inch drill bit

- hammer + nail

- hypodermic needles that fit your syringe (if not included)

*A large pot can be used as an alternative if you don't have a pressure cooker. Make sure the pot has a tight-fitting lid. A 3-piece steamer is ideal as the basket insert can be used to keep the jars off the bottom of the pot during sterilization.

Ingredients:

- 10 cc spore syringe

- brown rice flour

- vermiculite

- spring water

- perlite

Sterilization Equipment:

- air disinfectant

- butane/propane torch lighter (a regular gas lighter will work too)

- 70% Isopropyl rubbing alcohol

- paper towels

- laboratory gloves (optional)

- surgical face mask (optional)

Instructions:

NOTE: Before starting any of these methods, you should thoroughly sterilize your room and growing station. Spray the room with disinfectant and wipe down all surfaces and equipment using paper towels applied with rubbing alcohol. Take a shower and put on clean clothes. To be extra secure, brush your teeth, tie your hair back if it's long, wash your hands with antibacterial soap, and put gloves and a mask on.

Step 1: Preparation

1. Using the hammer and nail, poke four holes into the lid of each jar, making sure the holes are spaced evenly around the perimeter.

2. Add ½ cup of vermiculite and ¼ cup of water to the mixing bowl and mix thoroughly. Use the strainer to drain any excess water away.

3. Still in the bowl, add ¼ cup of brown rice flour to the mix and combine thoroughly.

4. Fill the first jar with this mix, to about half an inch from the rim. Take care not to pack it too tightly.

5. Sterilize the exposed half-inch using rubbing alcohol and then cover it with a layer of dry vermiculite to protect it from contaminants.

6. Repeat these five steps for the remaining nine jars.

Fun Fact: Adding a layer of dry vermiculite was Psilocybe Fanaticus' particular innovation. He discovered that doing this greatly improved protection from airborne contaminants as well as regulating moisture levels.

Step 2: Sterilization

1. Screw on the punctured lids and cover the whole jar with aluminum foil. Make sure the foil is large enough to cover your jar's mouth. It should run down the sides to about half the height of the jar.

2. Use your fingers to secure the foil tighter around the lip of the lid to prevent water and condensation from getting in through the holes.

Top tip: If the lid of your mason jar has a removable disc, turn this disc upside down so that the rubber edge is facing upwards and the jagged edges of the punched holes are facing down. Later on, this will allow you to adjust the tightness of the lid without taking the whole thing off. This is a safer and more efficient way to moderate airflow.

3. Place the metal rack inside the pressure cooker and arrange the jars on top. Elevating the jars from the base will prevent the glass from cracking or burning under the high temperatures. If you don't have a metal rack that fits, you could also use the jar lid rings (without the middle discs) to elevate the jars from the bottom of the pot or pressure cooker.

4. Fill the pressure cooker with about an inch or 2.5cm of tap water and bring slowly to a boil over the next 15 minutes. This will avoid cracking the jars. Make sure the jars stay upright.

5. Put the lid on and let the jars steam for 60 minutes (or 90 minutes if using a pot). Ideally, the jars will steam at 15psi, but if you are using a regular pot don't worry too much about reaching this exact number. The jars are small enough for the heat to penetrate and sufficiently sterilize them.

6. Once finished, leave the foil-covered jars to cool in the pressure cooker for at least 3 hours. You can leave it also leave it overnight. The jars must be cool to the touch before you inoculate them. If you are using a pressure cooker, be careful not to open it before it depressurizes as this can be very dangerous.

Step 3: Inoculation

1. Use the torch lighter to heat the syringe's needle until it is red hot. Once it has cooled, wipe it with rubbing alcohol.

2. It can help to give the syringe a little shake before injecting. This allows the psilocybin spores to spread out evenly.

3. Take out your first jar and remove the foil. Insert the syringe through one of the holes until it is touching the side of the jar. Inject about ¼ cc (a few drops) of the spore solution, making sure that the needle is below the level of dry

vermiculite. If the needle is not deep enough, you risk the spores being absorbed by the innutritious top layer of vermiculite. If this happens, they will not germinate.

4. Repeat this for the other three holes. You should use about 1 cc for each jar. A 10 cc syringe should therefore be perfect to inoculate your 10 jars.

5. Once all four holes have been injected into, cover them with micropore tape and place the jar to the side. There is no need to put the foil back on now.

6. Repeat this process with the rest of the jars, making sure to sterilize the needle with heat and alcohol in between inoculating each jar. During the inoculation stage, it is important to turn off any air conditioning and close all the windows.

Top tip: I have used a spore syringe as the method for inoculation here due to its popularity and ease of use. It is worth noting, however, that spore syringes have a bad reputation for harboring contaminants, which can develop and expand faster than the spores can germinate. Using a liquid culture is the surest way to avoid contamination at this stage. It will also lead to a faster and more vigorous rate of colonization. Find out more about liquid cultures in **Chapter 9: Preparing a Spore Syringe, Liquid Culture, and Others**.

Step 4: Incubation and Colonization

1. Find a warm, dark, clean place to put your inoculated jars. Optimal temperatures are 25–28°C (77–82°F) but average room temperature should be okay. Do not place your jars in direct sunlight.

2. Now you wait for the mycelium to grow! You should start to see the white, fluffy structure after the first week, but it can sometimes take up to two weeks to appear. The mycelium will grow outwards from your four inoculation sites.

3. After 2–4 weeks your jars should be fully colonized. You will know if they are as the substrate will be completely covered in white mycelium. Consider it a success if half your jars have been colonized. This is one of the reasons for inoculating so many - at least a few are likely not to take.

4. Leave the colonized jars to sit for a further seven days to allow the mycelium to strengthen. This is known as consolidation.

Step 5: Prepare the Fruiting Chamber

1. Using the electric drill, make a series of quarter-inch holes in the clear plastic box. The best way is to drill systematically, leaving two inches between each hole, and covering the sides, lid,

and bottom. A top tip is to drill from the inside out, as this will prevent the plastic box from cracking.

2. Secure the box in a way that allows for air to flow underneath. You might want to place something underneath the box to catch any excess moisture.

3. Once your fruiting chamber is set up, place the perlite into the strainer and wash it in sterilized cold water. Allow any excess water to drain.

4. Spread the perlite over the bottom of your fruiting chamber. Continue washing and layering the perlite in this way until you have a pile about 4–5 inches (10–12 cm) deep. Perlite helps to promote more evaporation, which is good for humidity levels.

Step 6: Fruiting

1. Open the jars and scrape the layer of dry vermiculite away without damaging the colonized substrate, which is referred to as a "cake" in this state.

2. Disinfect a table surface and place the lids down. Rest the jars upside down on their respective lids and tap down on the base to gently dislodge the cake. You should then be able to lift up the jar to release the cakes intact on their lid, which can now be used as a bed in the fruiting chamber.

3. One by one, carefully rinse the cakes under the cold tap to get rid of any loose vermiculite. Ensure your hands have been disinfected beforehand. Also, depending on the water quality of your region, you may want to boil and cool the water before using it for this step and the next one. This is to ensure the water is free from contaminants.

4. Now the cakes must be soaked in sterilized water to rehydrate. This is because they have been kept in an airtight container for weeks and may have already used up all the available moisture for the mycelium to grow. Your cakes will tend to float on the water so make sure you use a large pot or container with a lid to keep them submerged. Fill it with lukewarm water and place the cakes inside. If you want you can weigh the cakes down with a smaller pot or a similar heavy item. Leave for 24 hours.

   Psilocybe cubensis doesn't need a cold shock because it is a tropical species, but depending on the species you are cultivating, you may want to use cold water or place the container in the fridge during this dunking process. The cold water exposure is meant to mimic the temperature of autumn rain, which is the time of year when most species of mushrooms tend to fruit.

5. After this, fill your mixing bowl with more dry vermiculite. To be extra safe, you can bake the

vermiculite beforehand at 160°C (320°F) for one hour. Sterilizing a jar of dry it in the pressure cooker will also work. These extra anti-contamination measures usually do not need to be taken if the dry vermiculite is brand new and fresh from the bag.

6. Ensure your surface is disinfected before removing the cakes from the water and placing them down. Coat each cake in vermiculite by rolling it around the mixing bowl. This helps to retain moisture.

7. Once all the cakes are fully coated, prepare a square of aluminum foil for each one. They should be cut big enough that the cake can sit comfortably on them without touching the layer of perlite. Alternatively, you can continue to use the lids of the jars for the cakes to sit on

8. Distribute the foil squares or jar lids evenly inside the fruiting chamber and place a cake on top of each one.

9. Spray the sides of the chamber with water mist and fan the lid a few times before closing. Fresh air is very important as it checks any excessive levels of CO_2 and hastens the evaporation of moisture from the substrate. Both are pinning triggers. Stale air, on the other hand, will promote mold growth.

10. Throughout the fruiting stage, the growing chamber should be kept moist. Mist the bottom layer 3–4 times a day to maintain humidity and fan the lid after each misting. Humidity levels must be kept high at all times, at least 85%. A good way to check for this is to look for water droplets forming inside your chamber.

11. The only thing left to do now is to place your growing chamber in an area with good ventilation and enough indirect sunlight (or white fluorescent light) for around 12 hours a day.

Step 7: Harvesting

1. Watch for your mushrooms! They will start to appear as small white bumps, or "pins." This process is called pinning and it can take between 7–14 days until your mushrooms are ready for picking.

2. Make sure you harvest the mushrooms before they are fully mature as they start to lose their potency after that. The prime time to harvest is just before the veil underneath the mushroom cap breaks. You want the caps to be conical, not flattened out.

3. Cut the mushrooms close to their base. Again, make sure to disinfect whatever sharp utensil you use.

Once harvested, your mushrooms should be eaten immediately. If you want to keep them for later, they must be dried. See **Chapter 12** for how to dry your mushrooms effectively. This will apply to all methods.

If you are enjoying this book so far, it would mean a lot to me if you could take a minute to review or rate it on the respective platform you acquired it from. Did you know that just 0.5 - 1% of readers do actually end up leaving a review? I have to admit that I used to not be that 1%, but now I do it different since I know how meaningful this can be to independent writers.

Chapter 5: Uncle Ben's Tek (Spider-Man Tek) Method

Uncle Ben's Tek revolutionized home cultivation. The use of ready-made rice meant growers no longer needed to prepare their own grain medium or sterilize the bulk substrate in a pressure cooker, eliminating two lengthy, error-prone stages. It is also incredibly budget-friendly; depending on what you already have lying around the house, you could spend less than $100 on this tek. It's ideal for beginners.

What you need:

Equipment:

- 5 x 6-quart plastic tubs (2 bags per tub)*

- hand drill + 1.5-inch hole saw

- Poly-Fil

- 5-gallon bucket + lid

- micropore tape

- mist spray bottle

- hole punch

- knife

- scissors

- black bin bags

- hypodermic needles that fit your syringe (if not included)

*The IKEA Samla 1-gallon tubs have proven to be extremely effective.

Ingredients:

- 10 cc spore syringe

- 10 bags of Uncle Ben's brown rice

- 100% coco coir brick

- distilled water

Sterilization Equipment:

- air disinfectant

- 70% Isopropyl rubbing alcohol

- paper towels

- butane/propane torch lighter (a regular gas lighter will work too)

- laboratory gloves (optional)

- surgical face mask (optional)

Instructions:

First, a reminder to properly sterilize your workspace before starting (this includes your own body!) Use the air disinfectant and wipe down the table surface and any tools you are using with rubbing alcohol. It also helps to wipe down the outside of the Uncle Ben's rice bags.

Step 1: Inoculation

1. Once you have sterilized your bags, break up the rice inside with your hands. The rice should feel loose and squidgy, not clumped up.

2. Give your spore syringe a shake to evenly distribute the spores. Then sterilize the needle using the torch lighter. Heat until the needle glows red.

3. Once cooled, stick the needle through the plastic into the center of the bag and inject 0.5–1 cc of spore solution into the rice grains. Cover the hole with micropore tape immediately.

4. Using a hole punch, make six more holes close to the top of the bag to enable gas exchange. Cover each hole with micropore tape directly after puncturing.

5. Repeat this process for the remaining nine bags, taking care to flame-sterilize the syringe's needle before each inoculation.

Step 2: Incubation and Colonization

1. Once all the bags of rice have been inoculated, place them in a warm, dark place. Shelves or closets work well. Avoid places like kitchen cupboards and bathrooms. As I mentioned in the PF Tek, optimal temperatures for the colonization phase are 25–28°C (77–82°F) but the mycelium should still grow successfully at room temperature.

2. The mycelium should take between 2-4 weeks to fully colonize the rice grains. Once the bags are about 30% colonized they need to be given a shake. You can check this by looking through the bottom of the bag or feeling for dense, compact areas (where the mycelium has colonized).

3. If you feel 30% colonization has been reached, shake the bags to break up the mycelium and redistribute it to uncolonized areas. Don't panic if the mycelium appears blueish the following day, this is most likely bruising and not contamination. After 24 hours, the mycelium will recover and continue colonizing faster than ever!

4. To check the bags are fully colonized, shake them gently: you shouldn't feel any loose grains, just one solidified mass. If there are no green, yellow, or red colors present it means there is no contamination and you can move on to the next step!

Step 3: Pasteurization

1. Place the coco coir brick into the 5-gallon bucket. Boil ¾ gallon of distilled water and add it to the coco coir (boiling distilled water may seem like overkill but it can be risky using tap water!)

2. Stir the coco coir and water using a sterilized knife. Try to combine as well as possible. You may need to add more boiling water to fully break the coco coir up but take care not to completely soak it through.

3. Put the lid on the bucket and leave it to cool overnight. Now your bulk substrate has been pasteurized.

Step 4: 'Birth' the Cakes

Top tip: The coco coir increases in weight once you add water, so 50 g will become roughly 250 g. The ratio of spawn to bulk substrate only affects how fast the latter is colonized. While fast colonization means a lower risk of contamination, this is not such an issue with coco coir as it already has a relatively low risk of contamination. Therefore, you shouldn't have to use less of it to make up for its increase in weight. Two quarts of coco coir to one quart of spawn should be perfectly safe. Some growers even go up to a ratio of 4:1 or 5:1. "Spawn" just means a grain medium that has been fully colonized by mycelium.

1. Using the hand drill, make two 1.5-inch holes on each side of your plastic tub, about five inches up from the bottom. Then drill a 1.5-inch hole on each end (you should have six in total). Drill from the inside out as this will prevent the plastic from cracking. Once you have cleared all the debris away, stuff the holes with Poly-Fil.

2. Fold a black bin bag into the tub so that it covers the bottom and reaches 3–4 inches up the sides. This will prevent side pinning as mushrooms grow toward the light.

3. Add a 1-inch layer of the hydrated coco coir. You can test to see if it's perfect by squeezing a handful of coco coir over the bucket. Only a few droplets should come out.

4. Cut open a colonized rice bag and check for contamination. You should have a cake covered in healthy, white mycelium staring back up at you. Gently brush away any uncolonized rice grains.

5. Using your hands, crumble the cake into the layer of coco coir. It is crucial that you have either thoroughly sanitized your hands here, or you're wearing fresh gloves. The cake should be broken up as finely as possible and mixed thoroughly with the coco coir substrate.

6. Add another layer of coco coir to the tub and mix vigorously. The combination of grain spawn and substrate should now be 2–4 inches deep.

7. Pat the mix down and smooth out the surface. Sprinkle another layer of coco coir on top so that all the colonized grain has been covered. This should be no more than a ¼ inch and also smoothed down. Like in the PF Tek, this will act as a barrier against airborne contaminants and help to maintain moisture.

8. Repeat this process with the rest of the cakes. You should be able to fit two in each plastic tub.

Step 5: Fruiting

1. Allow your tubs to colonize about 75% of the surface before triggering the fruiting conditions. Essentially, put the lids on and leave them undisturbed for at least 48 hours. Let the mycelium do its thing.

2. Once the tubs are 75% colonized, take off the lid and put it back upside down. This is called "flipping"—it allows controlled amounts of air to flow into the tub, providing vital oxygen for the mushrooms during the fruiting stage. Moreover, sticking to our strategy of mimicking nature conditions, ensure the tub has some indirect sunlight or place an LED light above the

container for around 8-16 hours per day. Even though mushrooms do not need light to grow, it helps to direct them as they grow upwards. This is why the IKEA tubs are the best; they have clear plastic lids so the light can get through the top.

3. Mist the sides of the box with water frequently enough that the condensation never fully evaporates. Once pinning occurs, make sure you are not spraying directly onto the substrate or pins. If blue bruising starts to appear on the mushrooms, it indicates a build-up of CO_2. Reposition the lid to allow more oxygen in.

Step 6: Harvesting

1. Once pinning occurs, your mushrooms should be ready to harvest 1–2 weeks later. Make sure you harvest the fruits before they fully mature as they start to lose their potency after that. The prime time to harvest is just before the veil underneath the mushroom cap breaks.

2. Use a sterilized knife or scalpel to cut the mushrooms at their base. Cut as close to the substrate as possible as any stumps left will rot and potentially interfere with the mycelium. Remove any detritus attached to your mushrooms.

Either enjoy your mushrooms right away or dry them properly to be consumed later. Again, you can consult **Chapter 12** on the different drying methods.

Chapter 6: Monotub Tek Fruiting Chamber Method

The Monotub Tek may appear more advanced than the previous two teks, but once the initial setup is complete, it actually requires less manual labor. The monotub will ensure high humidity levels, while the holes that are drilled into the container will allow for appropriate air ventilation and gas exchange.

It is also cheap and produces very generous harvests. For these reasons, it is a favored method among mushroom cultivators and is often referred to as the most efficient and lucrative way to grow mushrooms at home.

What you need:

Equipment:

- large Sterilite plastic box, 55-60L
- large tote
- black bin bag
- micropore tape
- knife
- large spoon
- hand drill + 2-inch hole saw
- pressure cooker, or large pot
- poly-Fil
- mist spray bottle
- large oven bag
- 20L bucket + lid
- hypodermic needles that fit your syringe (if not included)

Ingredients:

- 10 cc spore syringe
- grain bag*

- ½ brick of coco coir

- 5L of coarse vermiculite

- 3.75L cow manure

- distilled water

*In this method, I will use a pre-prepared grain bag to show you a different approach. You can purchase this bag online. Millet and wheat berries work well as a medium for this tek. If you decide to follow your own method to prepare mushroom spawn, bear in mind that you will need around 5L of whatever grain medium you choose.

Sterilization Equipment:

- air disinfectant

- 70% Isopropyl rubbing alcohol

- paper towels

- butane/propane torch lighter (a regular gas lighter will work too)

- laboratory gloves (optional)

- surgical face mask (optional)

Instructions:

Again, just a reminder to thoroughly sterilize everything before getting started. You can never be too careful!

Step 1: Inoculation

1. Wipe down the table surface you are using with rubbing alcohol and flame sterilize the syringe's needle until it is red hot. Wait for it to cool before inoculating.

2. The purchased grain bag should have an injection port. Give your syringe a little shake before injecting 5cc of spore solution through the injection port.

3. Some injection ports will self-seal, but if not, cover the hole with micropore tape.

Step 2: Incubation and Colonization

1. Allow your grain to colonize, keeping temperatures at around 25–28°C (77–82°F). As I said before, don't worry if your room is a little cooler than this, the mycelium should still grow successfully at room temperature. Keep the bag in a dark place. This is necessary as light is a pinning trigger that will be used later on to "shock" the mycelium.

2. Watch as the mycelium starts to grow outwards from the inoculation point and spread through the bag. When it has covered about a third of the bag, gently break up the colonized grain so that it mixes with the uncolonized parts. This greatly accelerates the rate of colonization.

3. When your bag is completely covered in white mycelium, it is ready. This should take about 2–4 weeks.

Step 3: Prepare the Monotub

1. Using the hand drill, make a series of 2-inch holes around the tub. These air holes need to be above the substrate level (make sure the bottom of the holes sit just above the halfway line). Space the holes about 8 inches apart, making sure you have at least one hole on both ends. Drill from the inside out as this will prevent the plastic from cracking.

2. Fold the black bin bag so that it fits snugly at the bottom of your tub. It should come about halfway up the side of your tub. This is the same level that your bulk substrate will sit at.

Top tip: The bin bag is to line the bottom of the tub so that the mushrooms don't grow down or sideways. It is very difficult to harvest these mushrooms, and many of them become stunted as they don't have enough room to grow. While this isn't a huge problem, it is better to prevent it in the first place so as not to waste the mycelium's energy.

3. Now sterilize the whole tub by wiping it down with paper towels doused in rubbing alcohol. Don't forget the lid!

Step 4: Prepare the Bulk Substrate

1. Place the ½ brick of coco coir into the 20L bucket. Add 1.75L of boiling water, replace the lid and leave to sit for 15 minutes.

2. After that, break up the mixture with a large spoon so that it is thoroughly combined. Replace the lid once more and leave it to hydrate for a further hour.

3. In the large tote, combine the 3.75L of cow manure and 5L of coarse vermiculite and mix thoroughly. Then add the coco coir you prepared earlier. Mix until everything is evenly distributed.

Step 5: Sterilization

1. Transfer your substrate to the oven bag and seal it, making sure there is no excess air in the bag.

2. Using a sterilized knife, pierce a few holes in the top of the bag and cover them with micropore tape.

3. Place the bag into the pressure cooker and boil at 103kPa for 1 ½ hours. After this, leave the bag in there to cool overnight.

Step 6: Load Up the Monotub

1. Sprinkle a layer of the bulk substrate into the bottom of your tub until it is 1 inch deep. Add a layer of colonized grain or spawn on top.

2. Continue layering the tub like this until you reach the top of the bin liner.

3. Tightly plug the holes with Poly-Fil and place the lid on the tub. You must now wait for the spawn to colonize the bulk substrate. This usually takes 10-14 days. Keep the tub in a warm place with indirect sunlight. Bright light conditions can cause the mycelium to start fruiting prematurely, taking away from the mycelium reaching full growth.

Step 7: Fruiting

1. Once the surface of the substrate has turned completely white, watch for signs of pinning. This is signaled by clumps of white hyphae forming on the surface.

2. In the large tote, make up a casing layer by combining three parts vermiculite and one part distilled water. Make sure the tote has been washed and sterilized since it was last used. Mix thoroughly until the vermiculite is suitably hydrated.

3. Remove the tub lid and sprinkle a layer of hydrated vermiculite on top of the substrate, no more than 1 inch thick.

4. Generously mist the walls of the tub and replace the lid, this time leaving it slightly askew so that more air can get in. Try to keep a constant temperature of 22–24°C (71–75°F) and if you have a fan use it to produce a nice continuous flow of fresh air to "activate" the fruiting process. You should start to see mushrooms forming within the next 7–14 days.

Step 8: Harvesting

1. Harvest your mushrooms just before the veil underneath the cap breaks. Ensure you sterilize any tool used to cut the mushrooms from the substrate.

As mentioned in the previous two teks, you can either eat your mushrooms freshly picked or dry them and save them for later. See **Chapter 12** for how to do this properly and not let your hard work go moldy!

Chapter 7: Martha Tent Tek Method

A Martha Tent is a fruiting chamber that controls growing conditions in a similar way to a greenhouse. In this method, the grower has direct control over two of the four key areas of growing mushrooms: moisture and air exchange. This is done by placing sensors in the tent to monitor humidity and CO_2 levels. These sensors are rigged up to a humidifier and exhaust fan, respectively, which automate the tent's environment accordingly.

As for the other two key factors, light exposure can be taken care of by simply placing the tent in a strategic position, and temperature can be controlled by choosing an appropriate room (although bear in mind the tent will be slightly warmer inside). So you can see why the Martha Tent Tek is a real game-changer. It allows the cultivator to come the closest to perfectly mimicking natural growing conditions. Bear all of this in mind when you're setting it up, and it will not disappoint you. Use this method if you want to get serious and start producing mushrooms en masse.

What you need:

Equipment:

- indoor greenhouse tent that fits 4–5 shelves

- drip tray (if the greenhouse doesn't come with a bottom plate)

- ultrasonic humidifier*

- humidity sensor

- negative pressure exhaust fan

- CO_2 sensor

- ventilation hose

- filters

- duct tape

- hose clamps

- scissors

- aluminum tape

*You will need a humidifier that can be controlled by a separate controller. The low-tech option for providing a humid micro-environment is either using a tray of perlite or spraying a few times a day with sterilized water. Nevertheless, I would still recommend getting a humidity controller.

Instructions:

Step 1: Build your Greenhouse Tent

- Assembling your greenhouse tent is a simple process of following the supplier's instruction manual. If the tent did not come with a bottom plate, place the drip tray underneath. This will catch any excess moisture throughout the growing process.

- Choose a suitable location for your tent. There must be a power supply nearby and the tent should have access to indirect daylight. If you are growing your mushrooms in a closet or basement you will have to rig up artificial lighting. LEDs are the best as they are energy-efficient and don't produce a lot of extra heat. Ensure that the room you choose to put your tent in has a fresh air supply and stays at the right temperature.

Step 2: Attach the Humidifier

- A hose will run from the humidifier to the greenhouse tent. Cut a very small hole in one of the upper corners of the tent and feed the hose through a little bit. Make sure you don't position it to spray mist directly onto the mushrooms.

- Fix it in place and seal around the hole using duct tape.

- The humidifier itself can rest beside the tent on the floor. If the hose isn't long enough you can place the humidifier on a box or a small table.

Step 3: Attach the Exhaust Fan

- On the other side of the tent, fit the exhaust hose. Cut a small hole at the bottom of the tent so that the hose can be fed through as tightly as possible.

- Connect the hose to the exhaust fan (the two should have come together) and seal with aluminum tape. Similarly to the humidifier, the exhaust fan can just rest on the floor next to the tent.

Step 4: Attach Filters

- Inside the tent, attach a filter to the end of the exhaust hose and secure it with a hose clamp. This is to stop the spores from being sucked out and sprayed into your house.

- Alternatively, you can direct the other end of the exhaust hose outside by setting your tent up near a window. Some cultivators prefer to do this as it avoids pumping CO_2 back into the room. This is perfectly fine too, but you still want a good filter attached to the exterior end. This will prevent insects and other contaminants from getting inside your tent.

Step 5: Add the Sensors

- Try to place your humidity sensor in the middle of the tent. You could dangle it from the middle shelf, for example.

- The CO_2 sensor can go on one of the lower shelves. Place it at the back of the tent so it's not in the way.

- Connect the humidity sensor to the humidifier and the CO_2 sensor to the exhaust fan. This creates a fully automated system that will use the sensors to maintain optimal humidity and CO_2 levels without you having to monitor them. This is the magic of the Martha tent.

Step 6: Establish the Parameters

- Use the controllers to set the parameters for the CO_2 and humidity levels inside the tent. For *Psilocybe cubensis*, humidity levels should be at 95–100% during incubation and colonization. Once the pinning stage has begun the humidity should be reduced to 90–95%. CO_2 levels should be kept at 5,000–10,000 ppm until pins start to appear. They should then drop to below 5,000 ppm while the mushrooms are fruiting.

Congratulations! You have successfully set up your fruiting chamber. The amazing thing about Martha tents is they are able to fruit mushrooms regardless of the method you used to colonize the substrate. Therefore, you could use any of the methods outlined in the previous three chapters and then transfer your jars, tubs, or bags to the Martha tent for pinning, fruiting, and harvesting!

Chapter 8: Outdoor Cultivation

So far, we have looked at methods for cultivating mushrooms indoors. Generally speaking, this is the route most home growers take, especially beginners. However, there are ways to grow your mushrooms outside, and this chapter will take you through one of the methods for doing this. I have chosen what is sometimes referred to as the "wood chip method," but once you get the gist of it, you can experiment with substituting materials and colonizing larger areas.

The best part about outdoor cultivation is that once you have set up your patch and inoculated it, you can more or less sit back and let nature do its thing. If all goes well, the mycelium will establish itself in the local ecosystem and do what it does best; spread. Nature permitting, you can also expect to get repeat harvests in the years following the first year of inoculation with little to no interference from you.

What you need:

Equipment:

- cardboard

- 2 x large buckets

- large plastic bag

- strainer

- garden hose
- sterilized fork

Ingredients:

- mushroom spawn (purchased online or your own)
- sawdust*
- sterilized wood chips
- straw (optional)

*Sawdust from hardwood trees is best for *Psilocybe cubensis*. Some examples are oak, ash, poplar, elm, or beech.

Instructions:

Step 1: Inoculate the Sawdust

1. First, you will need to inoculate your sawdust with the purchased grain spawn. Keep in mind that two square meters of mushroom patch will require about 2.5 kg of sawdust spawn. Think about how big you want your patch to be and weigh out things accordingly.

2. Place the sawdust in a bucket and pour boiling water over it until it's completely submerged.

Leave for 10–15 minutes. This should sufficiently pasteurize it.

3. Drain the excess water from the sawdust using a strainer. In the other bucket, layer the sawdust and grain spawn and mix thoroughly using a sterile fork.

4. Place the layered bucket in a large plastic bag and tie it at the top. This will keep it humid.

5. Once a day, untie the bag to allow fresh oxygen in. After 2–4 weeks the sawdust should be fully colonized and ready to be introduced to your outdoor mushroom patch.

Step 2: Pick your Spot

1. While you wait for the mycelium to colonize the sawdust, you can choose your growing spot. Most people pick a patch in their garden as it's the most practical. If you live near a secluded piece of woodland or forest this will make for an excellent spot too. Wherever you pick, you must consider several important factors. Firstly, the spot must have access to indirect light. An area where trees or shrubs provide dappled sunlight is the best.

2. Secondly, proximity. If you are not growing in your garden, your spot must be close to your house. This is because you will have to access it

regularly towards the end of the fruiting stage so as not to miss prime harvesting time. It should be easy to get to but secluded from other people.

3. Finally, the ground must be moist enough for the mycelium to thrive. An area with a slight slope to it is even more ideal as this will naturally facilitate water flow.

Step 3: Set up the Patch

1. Once you've chosen your spot, remove any surrounding debris, including weeds and other plant matter. You don't want any organisms competing with your mycelium for space and nutrients.

2. Once you have cleared your site, cover it in cardboard.

3. Layer the cardboard with 5 cm of wood chips, making sure they are distributed evenly.

4. Using a garden hose, sprinkle some water over the wood chips to moisten them.

Step 4: Introduce the Mycelium

1. It is now time to add your sawdust spawn! Apply a layer of the spawn onto the wood chips,

approximately 300g per square meter. Spread it out as evenly as possible.

2. Next, place a 2-inch/5 cm thick layer of wood chips down. Moisten with the hose again.

3. Cover this layer with another 300g of spawn and then add 3 cm, or just over an inch, of wood chips on top.

4. Continue alternating the layers like this until you have used up all of your spawn. You should finish with a pile of wood chips on top. Make sure to moisten each layer of wood chips with water as you go along.

5. Finally, cover the pile with more cardboard to help retain moisture. Some growers like to add a layer of straw here as an additional protective barrier. However, this can sometimes backfire as the straw may attract competing strains of fungi or other harmful molds. If you do decide to use it, sterilize it thoroughly beforehand and only apply a thin layer.

Et voilà! You have successfully set up an outdoor cultivation patch. As you can see, one of the great benefits of this method is that you barely have to worry about contamination. There's none of the obsessive cleaning and rigorous sterilization that indoor cultivation requires. The drawback is that you now have to wait much longer to receive your mushrooms. Once you have created your spawn and wood chip pile, it has to be left undisturbed for about six months while the mycelium acclimatizes. *Psilocybe cubensis* naturally fruits in late autumn and early winter. It is therefore best to begin this whole process at the beginning of the year. To play it safe, inoculate your sawdust in January, and it will certainly be ready to introduce to your patch by March.

With the onset of winter, a drop in temperature and increased rainfall will initiate fruiting in your patch. Should you experience an unusually warm or dry season that year, water the patch yourself twice a day. This should help trigger fruiting. Once mushrooms start to appear, they will grow quickly. Check the patch every day during fruiting to ensure you harvest at the opportune moment. Also, keep an eye out for any unwanted species of plant or fungi that may have invaded your patch.

Chapter 9: Continuing the Cycle

How to Collect Spores

One of the wonderful aspects of home cultivation is that once you've had a successful flush you can collect your own spores and the cycle can continue indefinitely. You'll never have to buy new spores again!

The easiest way to collect spores from a mushroom is to make a spore print, which I will take you through step by step. You can think of this as a bit like taking a mushroom's fingerprint.

Just like in the growing methods, it is incredibly important to follow sterile procedures here. If your spores are contaminated, you are setting up the whole next cycle for failure.

Spray the room with air disinfectant and wipe down your growing station and any equipment you are using. Thoroughly clean yourself too. Remember, if you prefer not to wear gloves and a mask, wash your hands with antibacterial soap every 20 minutes. Pick a small room or enclosed area to work in. In order to minimize airflow, ensure any windows are closed and all air conditioning is switched off.

What you need:

Equipment:

- aluminum foil

- scalpel

- wide mouth glass jar

Ingredients:

- fully mature mushroom

- sterilized water

Sterilization Equipment:

- 70% Isopropyl rubbing alcohol

- paper towels

- air disinfectant

- butane/propane torch lighter (a regular gas lighter will work too)

- laboratory gloves (optional)

- surgical face mask (optional)

Instructions:

1. To extract the spores you must first allow the mushroom to fully mature so that its cap has flattened out. A collection of dark, blueish-black deposits at the stem signals that the mushroom is ready for sporulation. Once it starts to drop its spores, you must act quickly so as not to lose any. The more spores you have on your print, the less likely it is to become contaminated.

2. Cut a piece of aluminum foil and wipe it down with rubbing alcohol. Similarly, flame-sterilize the scalpel before cutting into your mushroom. Try to cut the cap as close to the stem as possible to better expose the gills. Then place it onto the foil, gills facing down.

3. Place a few drops of sterilized water onto the mushroom cap and cover it with a glass jar. This will maintain a high humidity level, which helps the mushroom to eject more spores. The glass covering will also protect the print from airborne contaminants.

Fun Fact: The water droplets here mimic a symbiotic relationship that takes place between rain and fungi in the natural world. When rain falls onto mushroom caps, the water helps push the spores out into the air. Recent evidence has suggested that these spores can then act as nuclei for the formation of raindrops in clouds. So, the rain aids the fungi by spreading their spores and germinating new areas, and in return, the spores contribute to rainfall. This relationship can be seen most clearly in ecosystems like tropical rainforests, where there are dense populations of fungi.

4. There is no fixed rule for how long to leave the cap on the foil, but most cultivators leave theirs overnight at least. After leaving the mushroom cap printing onto the foil for 24 hours, I remove the cap and place a new glass jar over the spore print only. I then leave it for 12 hours. This helps to dry it out further. A small pack of silica gel can be taped to the inside base of the glass to absorb humidity in the air. This is a very effective way to dry out the spores without physically touching them.

5. When you return, you will see that the mushroom has deposited its spores onto the foil. Tear off a bigger piece of aluminum foil and make an envelope by folding it in half and double-folding the edges. Place your spore print into the makeshift envelope and store it in a cool, dark place. If done properly, your print can last for years.

An even better way to keep spores is in a spore syringe or spore vial. Read on to find out more about what these are and how they differ.

Preparing a Spore Syringe, Liquid Culture, and Others

Preparing a Spore Syringe

A spore syringe is simply a syringe that contains psilocybin spores held in distilled water. Once you have made a spore print, you can prepare your own spore syringe. This is perfect for the novice cultivator who wants to keep the inoculation process as sterile as possible.

What you need:

Equipment:

- 3–5 10 cc syringes

- hypodermic needles that fit your syringe (if not included)

- pressure cooker

- airtight plastic bag (Ziploc are great)

- shot glass or bowl

- tweezers

- scalpel

Ingredients:

- spore print

- distilled water

Sterilization Equipment:

- butane/propane torch lighter (a regular gas lighter will work too)

- 70% Isopropyl rubbing alcohol

- paper towels

- air disinfectant

- laboratory gloves (optional)

- surgical face mask (optional)

Instructions:

As always, remember to keep your workspace as clean as possible. Fully prepare and sterilize the surfaces, equipment, and yourself before starting.

1. Place the water and shot glass (or bowl) in the pressure cooker for 30 minutes to sterilize. If you are reusing an old syringe, sterilize it in the pressure cooker as well.

2. Allow everything to cool. The spores will die if they are mixed with water that is too hot.

3. Fill the shot glass with 10 ml of sterile water. Pick up your spore print with the tweezers and hold it over the glass. With your other hand, gently scrape some of the spores from the print into the water using a scalpel. Make sure that both the tweezers and scalpel have been flame-sterilized beforehand.

4. To distribute the spores, fill and empty your sterilized syringe two or three times before filling it for a final time. Pulling back the plunger will fill the syringe.

5. While it is not an exact science, I find that one spore print is enough to fill about 3–5 10 cc syringes. You can therefore repeat these steps for as many more syringes as your print can accommodate. Make sure you sterilize all of your equipment each time you start a new syringe.

6. Once you have filled your syringes, leave them at room temperature for 48 hours. This is so the spores have a chance to properly hydrate.

7. After this, place each syringe in an airtight plastic bag and store them in the fridge. In these conditions, a spore syringe can last between 6–12 months but try to use it within six months to be safe. Now you have your spores all set up and ready to go whenever you want to inoculate!

Spore Vials

Unlike spore syringes, spore vials are made out of glass, which prevents the spores from sticking to the edges due to static electricity, as can sometimes happen with plastic syringes. This creates issues when injecting spores after long-term storage. Additionally, spore vials have an airtight rubber cap that protects the solution inside from contaminants. Due to their size and shape, they can hold greater quantities of spores per milliliter and are also physically practical for storing, as they don't have needles that can bend or snap. Spore vials can last for up to two years if stored in the right conditions. Store them in the fridge or at a temperature of 2–8°C (35–46°F). Once you have used up all the solution inside, simply sterilize and reuse it!

Liquid Culture

A liquid culture is essentially mycelium grown in an aqueous solution composed of water fortified with extra nutrients like honey and malt extract. Psilocybin spores can be transferred directly from the spore print into this serum, which then becomes the growth medium for spore germination. Mushroom cultivators have found that this method greatly speeds up the germination process, often producing mycelium within a week of introducing the spores. This mushroom liquid culture can then be used to inoculate your substrate, and the mycelium will start to colonize almost immediately. Compare this with the 2–4 week incubation period that follows after the grain is inoculated with a regular spore syringe. In other words, you are skipping the spores-to-mycelium stage.

As well as being incomparably efficient, mushroom liquid culture is also much more resistant to contamination than spore syringes. This means you don't have to worry about buying a Still Air Box or going sterile-crazy when inoculating your substrate. Of course, sterile procedures should still be followed, but you are much more likely to succeed with a mushroom liquid culture.

Vials made by experienced mycologists are readily available and affordable online. Once you have purchased a liquid culture, you should keep it out of direct sunlight and store it at a temperature of 2–20°C (35–68°F). The other option is to make your own. The ingredients are cheap and easy to find; they may even be lying around your house already. Just bear in mind that making your own liquid culture can be a process prone to contamination. Follow sterile techniques as best as you can, and be prepared to give it more than one go. Your patience will pay off.

What you need:

Equipment:

- pressure cooker, or large pot with a tight-fitting lid

- glass jar + lid

- hammer and nail

- aluminum foil

- kitchen tongs

- ½ teaspoon measuring spoon

- black permanent marker pen

- scalpel

- marble (optional)

- magnetic stirrer + stir bar (optional)

Ingredients:

- sterilized spore syringe or spore print

- clear honey

- maple syrup or light corn syrup

Sterilization Equipment:

- butane/propane torch lighter (a regular gas lighter will work too)

- air disinfectant

- 70% Isopropyl rubbing alcohol

- paper towels

- laboratory gloves

- surgical face mask (optional)

Instructions:

Before starting, close all windows and turn off any air conditioning. You want the air in the room to be as still as possible. Spray the room with air disinfectant, and wipe down your workstation and any tools you'll be using. Make sure you are clean and wearing fresh clothes, and I would recommend using gloves.

Step 1: Preparation and Sterilization

1. Using the hammer and nail, make a small hole in the lid of the jar.

2. Fill your pot or pressure cooker with cold water and place the jar and lid (separated) inside. Bring to a boil, increasing the temperature gradually so as not to crack the glass.

3. Leave to sterilize for half an hour. Don't worry about putting the lid on the pot/pressure cooker at this point.

4. Wipe down the table surface and kitchen tongs with rubbing alcohol. Use the tongs to maneuver the glass jar so that it is ¾ full of boiling water. Remove it from the pot and rest it on the side. Do not turn the stove off at this point, keep the remaining water in the pot boiling.

5. Add ½ teaspoon of honey and ½ teaspoon of syrup to the boiling water in the jar. Adopt a ratio of one teaspoon of honey-syrup mixture for every 200 ml of water. Mix thoroughly.

Top tip: At this point, some cultivators like to drop a magnetic stir bar into the mix before sealing the jar up. This will come in handy later, as you can set up your jar on a magnetic stirrer, which will spin the stir bar around, agitating the liquid culture and prompting the mycelium to grow even faster. If you don't have this kind of equipment, dropping a marble into the mix can act as a suitable, albeit less effective, alternative.

6. Wipe the tongs down again and use them to extract the jar lid from the pot, where the water

should still be boiling. Use a wad of clean paper towels to screw the lid onto the jar.

7. Cover the jar in aluminum foil and secure it tightly over the lid. A top tip here is to mark where the hole is with a permanent marker so that you know for later.

8. Place the jar back into the pot of boiling water so that it is submerged halfway. Seal the lid on the top and reduce the heat. Leave it simmering like this for a further 30 minutes. If you are using a pressure cooker, cook for 20 minutes at 15 psi.

9. When the time is up, simply turn off the stove and leave the pot to cool overnight. Do not open the lid as this will expose the sterile environment inside to airborne contaminants.

Step 2: Inoculation

1. The next day, wipe down all of your surfaces and equipment with rubbing alcohol again. Remove the jar from the pot and place it down.

2. Flame sterilize the needle on your syringe until it is red hot. Find the marked spot on the foil and peel it back enough to uncover the hole in the lid. Working quickly, insert the needle and inject about 2 cc of spore solution (depending on how much serum you made, you can add more) before replacing the foil. For the spores and

serum ratio, the more spores you inject, the faster the incubation process will be. Simply don't skimp.

3. If you are using a spore print instead, flame sterilize the scalpel and loosen the lid of the jar. Scrape some spores off the print with your scalpel, lift the jar lid just enough to fit the scalpel in, and tap the spores into the serum. Seal the jar as quickly as possible.

Step 3: Incubation

1. After inoculating the jar with either spore syringe or print, give it a gentle swirl to mix the spores in evenly. Make sure you label it with the date of inoculation and type of strain used.

2. Store the jar in a warm, dark place (roughly 28°C, or 82°F). Repeat the swirling motion once a day to encourage the mycelium to spread.

Top tip: If you opted for the marble earlier, it will spin around the jar here and help to break up and spread the mycelium. You will have to repeat this manually each day. If you went with the magnetic stir bar, set your jar up on a magnetic stirrer. Once the mixture is spinning nicely, turn the setting down to low. Now sit back and relax!

3. After just a few days you will start to see hyphae forming. Within a week your liquid culture will

be ready for use. Always make sure to agitate it before drawing any solution out. This will ensure your mycelium is evenly distributed. When you are ready to use it, use a sterile syringe to extract the liquid culture through the same hole you used to inoculate it with spores.

Inoculating grain with a liquid culture follows the exact same process as inoculating with a spore syringe, so the next steps you know already. The only difference is that you will get a much faster colonization rate!

Chapter 10: Advanced Techniques: Beyond the Basics

Growing with Agar and Cloning Mushrooms

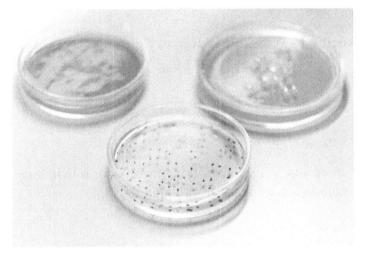

Once you've got the hang of making a spore print and preparing your own syringe or liquid culture, you can start thinking about working with agar. Agar is a jelly-like substance that comes from red algae. Although originally used in food recipes, agar has long been central to the study of microbiology as it creates the perfect environment for growing bacteria. Mycologists too have taken up the use of agar to grow and study fungi cultures. Although it can seem a little intimidating at first, once you grasp the fundamentals of growing with agar, it can become a fascinating and indispensable tool.

Below are three recipe variations for making agar. The first is just a basic mixture of agar and water, followed by two of the most commonly used recipes; potato dextrose agar (PDA) and malt extract agar (MEA). Pick whichever one you want to use before moving on to the instructions on how to grow with agar.

Recipe 1: Agar and Water

Ingredients:

- 5 g of agar powder*

- 200 ml of water

*Often sold as agar-agar. It is available for sale in most Asian supermarkets or health food shops.

Recipe 2: Potato Dextrose Agar (PDA)

Ingredients:

- 5 g of agar powder

- 5 g of dextrose*

- 200 ml of potato broth**

*Dextrose is a sugar made from corn, very similar to glucose. It is widely available in health food shops.

**You can make this by boiling 100 g of sliced potatoes (leave the skin on) in 500 ml of water for half an hour. Filter the broth through a clean tea towel until you get 200 ml of it.

Recipe 3: Malt Extract Agar (MEA)

Ingredients:

- 5 g of agar powder

- 200 ml of water

- 1 g of malt extract syrup

Growing with Agar

The usual friendly reminder here to sterilize each step of the way during this process. Unlike in the growing methods, you're not going to get away without using a Still Air Box here. It is a crucial piece of equipment for growing with agar and is part of this sterile technique. I would also recommend you wear gloves this time. Make sure you have thoroughly cleaned and disinfected yourself and your workspace before starting.

What you need:

Equipment:

- pressure cooker

- saucepan

- Still Air Box (SAB)

- laser temperature thermometer

- scalpel

- aluminum foil

- 350ml glass jar or beaker

- 10–15 clean takeout sauce containers (these are a cheap, easy alternative to Petri dishes)

Ingredients:

- spore print

- agar ingredients

- food coloring (optional)

Sterilization Equipment:

- 70% Isopropyl rubbing alcohol

- paper towels

- butane/propane torch lighter (a regular gas lighter will work too)

- laboratory gloves

- surgical face mask (optional)

Instructions:

PART 1: Preparing your Agar Dishes

Step 1: Make the Agar

1. Pour 200 ml of water into a saucepan (or 200 ml of potato broth if you're using the PDA recipe) and wait until it reaches 60–80°C (140–176°F). Add the rest of the ingredients, agar powder last.

2. Heat the mixture, stirring slowly and steadily to avoid the agar clumping. Once it starts to boil, take the saucepan off the heat straight away. You don't want to overcook the agar.

3. Pour it into the glass jar or beaker and cover the top with aluminum foil. At this point, if you want to add a few drops of food coloring, you can. Some cultivators like to do this as it makes it easier to spot contamination later, not to mention the fact that it makes the agar look prettier!

Step 2: Sterilization

1. Once the top has been sealed with aluminum, place the jar or beaker in the pressure cooker and cook for 30 minutes at 15 psi to sterilize it. Make sure you allow the pressure cooker to depressurize properly before removing the agar.

2. Agar will start to set at around 32–40°C (89–104°F), whereas its melting point is around 85°C (185°F). You need to wait for the agar to cool before pouring it into the containers to avoid accidentally melting the plastic. I recommend waiting until the agar has cooled to about 60°C (140°F) to reduce condensation and to be able to handle it better. Use the thermometer to keep checking until it is at the desired temperature. Ensure the thermometer is clean.

3. While you are waiting, sterilize the inside of your Still Air Box (SAB) and any tools you'll be using with paper towels doused in rubbing alcohol.

Step 3: Pour the Agar

1. Set up your takeaway sauce containers in the SAB. Make sure you can reach all of them comfortably. Loosen all of the lids a little so that they are resting on top but will be easy to remove.

2. Pour the agar into the containers, trying to distribute it evenly. A useful tip here is to stack

the containers on top of each other once you've filled and sealed them. This will lessen the amount of condensation forming on the bottom of the lids, lowering the risk of bacterial contamination.

3. Leave your agar dishes to cool in the SAB. If you intend to use them in the next couple of days, you can store them at room temperature. Otherwise, store them in the refrigerator.

PART 2: Germination and Contamination Control

Step 1: Introduce the Spores

1. Now that you have prepared all your dishes, you can introduce your spores and start growing some mycelium! First, wipe down the inside of your SAB with rubbing alcohol. Place the spore sprint (still enclosed in its aluminum envelope) and a couple of agar dishes inside the SAB.

2. Loosen the lids on your dishes but do not remove them.

3. Flame sterilize your scalpel using the torch lighter. Remember to do this outside of the SAB to avoid the Isopropyl igniting. Heat the scalpel until it glows red and then let it cool.

4. Gently open up the spore print, taking care not to touch the print directly.

5. Using the scalpel, scrape a little of the spore print onto the agar dish. You only need a few visible specks; each one holds hundreds of microscopic spores. If you are using a spore syringe instead of a print, make sure it is properly sterilized and then squeeze 1–2 drops onto the agar dish. Replace the lid immediately afterward.

6. Repeat this step with the other agar dish, making sure you flame sterilize the scalpel outside of the SAB beforehand. If you want to add spores to more of your agar dishes, I would add them to the SAB two at a time and follow the steps above. You'll want to keep at least five agar dishes spore-free. This is so they can be used later on to transfer healthy mycelium away from contaminated dishes. We will come to this in more detail in the next step.

Top tip: Label the agar dishes as you go. Include the strain of *P. Cubensis* used, e.g., Golden Teachers, the date, and the type of agar used. This last detail will help you compare the efficacy of different recipes in the future.

Step 2: Germination and Colonization

1. Store your dishes in a dark place at room temperature, approximately 18–26°C (64–79°F). As in the growing methods, you don't want the temperature too hot or too cold. The

former will encourage contamination and the latter will slow the growth of the mycelium.

2. The spores will start to germinate within a week of being introduced to the agar. However, it may take up to two weeks to see any visible mycelium growing. Keep checking on your dishes regularly.

3. It is likely that you will start to see contamination growing as well, but don't panic, the healthy mycelium can be cut out and moved to a clean dish. This is the beauty of growing on agar.

Step 3: Dealing with Contamination

1. If all of your dishes are contaminated to some degree, choose the dishes with the least visible contamination to make the transfer. Place it in the SAB along with a clean agar dish. Loosen the lid of the agar dish so that it can be removed easily.

2. Flame-sterilize your scalpel outside of the SAB and then take off the lid of your contaminated dish. Cut a bit of healthy mycelium out of the agar. You'll want to pick a section that's furthest away from the contamination and shows strong rhizomorphic growth (long strands of thick mycelium, as opposed to thread-like or fluffy).

3. Secure the sample on the end of your scalpel and with the other hand remove the lid from the

clean agar dish. Pop the sample onto the agar and replace the lid quickly.

4. You can keep transferring healthy mycelium over to new agar dishes in this way until you have a culture that is completely contaminant free. Do not put all of your eggs in one basket by transferring mycelium from a single dish. Rather, try to use several dishes in case there are any non-visible contaminants present. Allow the mycelium to grow until it has covered the entire surface of the agar and then store it in the fridge.

Cloning Mushrooms

If you look closely at a mushroom, you will see that it is made up of fibers called hyphae. This is also called tissue culture. Cloning is the process of extracting a sample of this tissue from a freshly harvested mushroom and continuing its genetics by growing it on agar. Cloning is useful as it skips the germination process and propels you forward 1-2 weeks into the growing cycle. Tissue cultures have a much lower contamination risk and are great for when you want to reproduce a strong, potent strain. For more involved mycologists, it is also a way to breed genetically superior mushrooms.

What you need:

Equipment:

- Still Air Box (SAB)

- scalpel

Ingredients:

- fresh mushrooms
- agar dishes

Sterilization Equipment:

- 70% Isopropyl rubbing alcohol
- paper towels
- butane/propane torch lighter (a regular gas lighter will work too)
- laboratory gloves
- surgical face mask (optional)

Instructions:

Step 1: Sterilization

1. Choose which specimen of mushroom you want to take the sample from and wipe it down with a paper towel soaked in alcohol.

2. Wipe down the inside of the SAB with rubbing alcohol and place your agar dishes and mushrooms inside.

3. Loosen the lid on the agar dish you are about to use but do not fully remove.

4. Outside of the SAB, sterilize the scalpel with a torch lighter until it glows red.

Step 2: Extract the Tissue

1. Back inside the SAB, split the mushroom apart with gloved hands, tearing it lengthways from the bottom.

2. Find a point in the middle of the stem and cut a small sample from the flesh with the scalpel. Using the innermost part of the mushroom is important as it contains tissue that has had the least environmental exposure.

3. Secure the sample on the end of the scalpel and quickly transfer it to the agar dish, lifting and replacing the lid as quickly as possible.

4. Repeat these steps for the other agar dishes, making sure to flame sterilize the scalpel each time. If you are using over five agar dishes, I would rub your gloved hands with Isopropyl alcohol halfway through and move on to another fresh mushroom. This is to ensure you keep

extracting clean samples. Take as many tissue samples from the fresh mushrooms as you can. This is because you will inevitably lose some dishes to contamination.

Step 3: Colonization

1. As before, store the dishes in a dark place at room temperature while the mycelium is growing. Over the next 1–2 weeks you will see the white hyphae branching out from the tissue sample.

2. Once the mycelium has fully covered the surface of the agar, store the dishes in the fridge until you are ready to spawn them out to grain.

Agar-to-Grain and Grain-to-Grain Transfers

Agar-to-Grain (A2G)

Once you have your fully colonized agar dishes, you can use them to inoculate a grain medium and start growing some mushrooms! This process is called Agar-to-Grain (A2G).

What you need:

Equipment:

- Still Air Box (SAB)
- scalpel
- micropore tape
- sharp tool (to make holes in the lids)

Ingredients:

- five pre-sterilized grain jars
- five colonized agar dishes

Sterilization Equipment:

- 70% Isopropyl rubbing alcohol
- paper towels
- butane/propane torch lighter (a regular gas lighter will work too)
- laboratory gloves
- surgical face mask (optional)

Instructions:

Before starting, wipe down the inside of the SAB and your gloved hands with rubbing alcohol.

1. Place all of the grain jars and agar dishes inside the SAB. Disinfect the lid of the first grain jar with alcohol just to be safe and then loosen it so it is easily removable.

2. Open your first agar dish and make a criss-cross pattern to cut it up. Ensure the scalpel has been flame sterilized beforehand.

3. Remove the lid from the first grain jar and drop the chunks of agar into it, squeezing the sides a little if the agar gets stuck. Replace and seal the lid immediately. You want to limit the amount of time the grain is exposed to the air as much as possible.

4. Outside of the SAB, give the grain jar a good shake to distribute the agar and spread out the inoculation points. This will speed up the colonization process.

5. Inoculate your remaining grain jars by adopting a ratio of one agar dish per grain jar. Like in the PF Tek Method, you should have a few holes in the lid of each jar covered with micropore tape to allow for essential gas exchange while the mycelium is growing. Remember, the breathing holes should be made before sterilizing the jar to

avoid excessive manipulation after sterilization. Store them in a dark place at room temperature.

6. You might notice at this point that everything follows the same process. Once the grain jars are roughly 30% colonized, tighten the lids and give the jars another good shake. This is to break up all the mycelium that had been growing and redistribute it around the jar.

7. The jars will take about 3–4 weeks to fully colonize.

Grain-to-Grain (G2G)

Grain-to-Grain transfers (G2G) are even more efficient than A2G. By transferring colonized grain over to uncolonized grain, you can grow mycelium incredibly fast and quickly multiply those favorable genetics. One colonized jar quickly becomes ten, and before you know it, you are looking at a harvest more bountiful than ever before!

What you need:

Equipment:

- Still Air Box (SAB)

Ingredients:

- 90–100% colonized grain jar
- 5 x pre-sterilized grain jars*

*G2G transfers work with any type of grain. Choose whichever works best for you.

Sterilization Equipment:

- 70% Isopropyl rubbing alcohol
- paper towels
- butane/propane torch lighter (a regular gas lighter will work too)
- laboratory gloves
- surgical face mask (optional)

Instructions:

Again, make sure you have wiped everything down with rubbing alcohol and put on disinfected gloves before starting.

1. Shake and tap the colonized jar to break up the spawn. This will make it easier to transfer. You may need to apply some force here as the mycelium will be holding the grain together.

2. Once the colonized grain is fully broken up, wipe the jar with alcohol and place it in the SAB, next to the one filled with normal grain. Loosen both of the lids.

3. Working quickly, remove the lids of both jars and pour about ⅕ of the colonized grain into the normal grain jar. Close and seal both lids immediately. Minimizing the amount of time either jar is exposed to the air will help avoid contamination.

4. Repeat these steps for the remaining four jars. Remember to give the new inoculated jars a thorough shake so that the mycelium is distributed evenly before storing them for colonization.

5. Once inoculated, leave the jars in a dark place at room temperature, approximately 18–26°C (64–79°F). The mycelium should colonize them in as little as 14 days. The rest of the process you will be familiar with by now!

Storing Inoculated Grain

As a general rule, inoculated grain (spawn) should be used as soon as possible. If you ever need to purchase mushroom spawn, I would recommend choosing a reputable supplier as geographically close to you as possible. This will minimize the chances of receiving malnourished and potentially contaminated mycelium. Storing spawn for long periods of time significantly decreases the quality of the mycelium and exposes it to contamination. If you must store it, refrigerate it at a temperature of 2–5°C (35–40°F). Humidity levels should be kept low, ideally in the 40–50% range, but certainly no more than 60%. This will slow the rate of decline enough for the spawn to last at least 3–4 weeks, although some have reported theirs lasting for up to two months in refrigerated conditions.

Bear in mind that the process of refrigeration can cause its own problems. For example, water droplets from condensation can carry contaminants to your spawn bags. Cooling fans, air filters, and other installations can harbor threatening dust particles and mold. Even the spores from other mushrooms can transport bacteria to the spawn bags, which is why you should never store spawn in the same refrigerator as other live cultures. In addition to all of this, bear in mind the fact that metabolic waste inevitably accumulates over time. To avoid contamination in general, treat your refrigeration unit or room with the same sterile procedures as in a laboratory. Disinfect the space regularly, and check the spawn bags every week for signs of contamination.

Chapter 11: Troubleshooting Cultivation Problems

This chapter will look at the most common cultivation problems and how to troubleshoot them. The table is roughly chronological in order, addressing problems as they would arise naturally throughout the growing process.

Problem	Explanation	Solution
The spores don't germinate on agar.	Spores may not be viable.	Acquire fresh spores.
Grain spawn is too hard to break up.	You may have added too much water.	Reduce water by 10–25%.
	Inappropriate grain medium.	Use rye grain. Add or increase gypsum.
	Over-incubation.	Use spawn earlier.

Glass jars crack or grow bags break.	This is usually during the sterilization/pasteurization process. If the spawn container is not of good quality, it may break under high temperatures and/or pressures.	Make sure you purchase high-quality equipment. Must be heat and pressure resistant.

Always elevate the jars/bags from the base of the pot during sterilization/pasteurization to prevent cracking.

Never increase the temperature too quickly, always gradually. You want to avoid extreme fluctuations. You may need to reduce temperature and pressure overall. |

The mycelium is not growing.	You may have over-sterilized your grains, meaning there are not enough nutrients for the mycelium to grow. This might also make it grow and then die back.	Reduce the sterilization time.
	Temperature was too high at the time of inoculation.	Allow the medium to cool down after sterilization, before inoculating it.
	Not enough moisture.	Increase moisture levels.
	Inadequate grain medium (even if you bought one of the recommended grains, the strain you're using might not be particularly receptive to it.	Try an alternative grain medium.

	The spores may not have germinated successfully. This is either because you didn't inoculate deep enough into the grains, or your spore syringe is faulty.	Always inoculate below the casing layer of the substrate. Acquire spores from a different source.
The mycelium grows only in patches.	Jar was not inoculated with enough spore solution/ mycelium culture. Mycelium hasn't been distributed throughout the grain adequately enough.	Increase the inoculation rate for each jar. Once the mycelium has covered 20–30% of the jar, shake it thoroughly to expose uncolonized areas to the inoculation points. You may have to do this at more frequent intervals if mycelium

		growth remains slow.
	Potential presence of bacterial contamination.	Sterilize the grain medium for longer next time.
Discoloration of the mycelium (off-white, pink, red, green, yellow, black). There may also be a presence of foul odors.	The substrate has been contaminated by bacteria or molds. This could be due to faulty spores, bad sterilization technique, or over-incubation.	Especially in the case of black mold, isolate the contaminated cake from the others. Wear gloves and a mask, and take care not to inhale any bacteria as it can be harmful. Seal the cake in a plastic bag and dispose of it in the trash. Do not compost. Find out which vector was the source of contamination (see **Chapter 2**) and improve your sterile technique for next time. Try

| | | using spores from a different source.

In the event of over-incubation, trigger the pinning process sooner next time. Old spawn is susceptible to contamination. |
|---|---|---|
| Blue bruising on the mycelium. | This does not necessarily mean contamination. Mycelium might bruise for a number of different reasons, e.g., when physically handled or pressed up against the grow box, or even during rehydration.

It can also be due to a build-up of CO_2 levels. | Handle the mycelium as little and as gently as possible. If bruising does occur, the mycelium should recover in a couple of days.

Increase airflow to allow more oxygen in. |

Bluing or yellowing of the substrate.	It is likely that your substrate is too dry, possibly due to excessive air exchange.	Increase humidity.
The mycelium has colonized the substrate, but pinning has not occurred.	Inadequate humidity levels. If humidity is not high enough, no pinning will occur.	Increase humidity. Mist the walls of the grow bag or monotub regularly (you can also mist the substrate directly prior to pinning and then fan it to promote evaporation, although not excessively. This is a pinning trigger).
	Lack of light.	Move the substrate to a place that has indirect sunlight. Alternatively, set up artificial lighting

		overhead. LEDs work best.
	Temperature is too high.	Lower the temperature. Many strains will need a temperature drop, or "cold shock," to trigger the pinning process.
Side pinning.	This is because the sides of the grow bag or tub are exposed to light, prompting the mushrooms to grow towards it.	Before spawning to bulk, line the base and bottom half of your monotub with a black bin bag or black paint.

Use a tub that has a see-through plastic lid so that the mushrooms are directed upwards by the light coming in. |

The mycelium isn't producing fruiting bodies.	Temperature is too high.	Reduce temperature. Mushrooms need a temperature drop to fruit successfully. Levels should not exceed 22–24°C (71–75°F) during the fruiting stage.
	Excessive CO2 levels.	Increase airflow to let more oxygen in.
	Substrate is not moist enough.	Mist the walls of the grow bag or monotub regularly.
	Grain medium wasn't fully colonized before being introduced to the bulk substrate.	Allow for a longer incubation/colonization time before spawning to bulk. The grain medium should be completely covered in white mycelium.

	Lack of light.	Make sure the substrate has access to either indirect sunlight or artificial lighting.
	Bad strain.	Source a new strain from a different source.
	Your substrate may have been contaminated by bacteria or parasitic fungi.	Make a new spawn.
Lots of mushrooms start to form, but few develop.	Faulty strain.	Acquire a better strain from a different source.
	Lack of nutrients in the substrate.	Use a different grain medium and/or bulk substrate.
	Lack of light or oxygen.	Re-position substrate so that it has access to indirect light. Increase airflow

		to let more oxygen in.
	Low humidity or pH balance	Increase humidity and ensure you have a proper medium.
	Excessive pinning.	Shorten pinning period by promoting fruiting conditions sooner.
The stems appear fuzzy.	This could be mycelium growing on the stems, a sign that there is not enough airflow.	Increase airflow to let more oxygen in. Be careful not to let humidity levels drop in doing so - humidity must be kept high.
The stems look long and skinny, often with underdeveloped caps.	Excessive CO_2 levels.	Increase the amount of oxygen to check the build-up in CO_2 levels.
	Inadequate light.	Adjust light conditions.

Stems are thin and hollow.	Temperature is too high.	Lower temperature. This will allow the specimen to slowly develop, but this time healthier.
Mushroom caps opening prematurely.	Lack of light.	Ensure the substrate has sufficient exposure to (indirect) light.
	Low moisture levels.	Spray the walls of the monotub or grow bag with water mist until the substrate looks suitably hydrated.
Cracked mushroom caps.	This could be because the air is too dry.	Increase moisture levels or use a base layer of perlite.
Once harvested, the mushrooms went moldy very quickly.	You might have harvested the mushrooms too late, when they were already mature.	Harvest sooner, just before the veil beneath the cap breaks

	Temperature is too high.	Keep the harvested mushrooms in the fridge. They will spoil faster in warm temperatures.
	Humidity levels too high, meaning the mushrooms were overly wet when harvested.	On harvest day, reduce the humidity several hours before picking.
	Proper storing technique was not implemented soon enough.	Either consume your mushrooms within 24 hours of picking, or dry and store them properly.
The substrate is unable to produce subsequent flushes after the first harvest.	Not enough water and nutrients left in the substrate.	Fortify the cake with more bulk substrate. You may need to break it apart and re-distribute. Allow the

		mycelium to recover and then re-initiate the pinning process.
	Substrate may have been infiltrated by competing organisms.	Find out which vector was the source of contamination (see **Chapter 2**) and improve your sterile technique for next time.
	Faulty strain.	Acquire a better strain from a different source.
	The mycelium was ruined by spores falling from matured mushrooms.	Harvest your mushrooms before they drop their spores as this indicates to the mycelium the end of the life cycle.

	You may also have simply missed your window of opportunity.	Once you have harvested, soak your substrate overnight and re-initiate the pinning process. Do not just leave it to come back later for another flush.

Chapter 12: Harvesting, Drying, and Storing Magic Mushrooms

The prime time to harvest your mushrooms is just before the veil beneath the cap breaks. After that, the caps flatten out and bluish-black spores begin to pool at the stem. This is a signal that the mushrooms have reached full maturity. It is commonly believed that they start to decline in potency after this point as they focus their energy on spreading their spores.

You must harvest before this happens. Not only will the power of the psilocybin diminish, but the spores will also start to drop onto your substrate and ruin the healthy mycelium. More specifically, the dropped spores will signal to the mycelium that its life cycle has been completed. Instead of producing more flushes, it will therefore start to break down and die.

To harvest, you can cut the mushroom close to the stem leaving a tiny stump behind, nothing complicated (just keep things clean). Once you have harvested your mushrooms, you need to consider how to store them. Left fresh, your mushrooms will go moldy within the week. Mushrooms contain a high volume of moisture and are made up of 90% water. Anything that is loaded with moisture attracts mold and bacteria, and once your mushrooms get infected, the mold can spread like wildfire. The only way to store them long-term is to dry them and keep them in a cool, dark place, but you must dry your mushrooms properly because even a tiny bit of moisture can cause microbes to contaminate your harvest. If done properly, they will retain their potency for years. It's best to dry and store them whole to avoid potency loss.

We want bone-dry mushrooms. However, you also have to be careful about what temperatures you use to dry your mushrooms to avoid potency loss. Many users suggest keeping the temperature below 212°F (100°C), but there is no real evidence at the time this book is being written that suggests psilocybin starts to degrade at any given temperature. We just know that psilocybin is sensitive to heat and that the degradation rate increases when the temperature increases, particularly over 212°F (100°C). Hence, we will try to avoid unnecessarily high temperatures.

Before you decide on a drying method, you will have to cut off any part of the stem that is covered in substrate and clean your mushrooms, wiping off any visible dirt.

Do not use water to clean them, it is not recommended because this increases the moisture levels and the risk of contamination and decomposition. After your mushrooms have been cleared, you can begin the drying process. Your goal is to dry your mushrooms to the point that they become brittle and break. We will first look at a couple of drying methods, and then we will explore storage.

Drying

Before moving to any drying method, you can first pre-dry your mushrooms to ensure better results. Pre-drying is easy. Place your mushrooms on a dry towel or piece of cardboard. If you use a towel, you may need to replace it several times to ensure no moisture is re-absorbed. Place this board or towel out of direct sunlight in a well-ventilated area (you can also help it with a fan).

The perfect conditions are around 86 °F (30 °C) and humidity below 55%. Once your mushrooms look wrinkly and feel rubbery when touched, the pre-drying process is complete. You can then move on to drying your mushrooms using one of the next methods.

Dehydrator

Dehydrating your mushrooms is the best way to dry them. While dehydrators are typically quite expensive, they are a useful investment because you can use them not only to dehydrate your mushrooms for microdosing but to also dehydrate other foods that you can snack on like strawberries, regular mushrooms for cooking, etc. Remember, heat and mushrooms are not great friends. The higher the temperature, the quicker the mushroom degrades and the more tryptamines diminish. Mushrooms also don't like sunlight. This is why you should use a dark towel to cover your mushrooms when air-drying them under the sun.

The larger mushrooms will go on the top ring tray (where heat is higher), while the smaller ones get placed on the bottom ring tray. Spread your mushrooms out on the dehydrator trays, ensuring none of the mushrooms are touching each other, and place the trays back in the dehydrator. If you are using a vertical dehydrator, put the biggest mushrooms closest to the fan and arrange them from medium to small going outwards, leaving the tiny mushrooms furthest from the fan. Set your dehydrator to 110°F or 40°C. This device uses gentle heat and constant airflow to remove the remaining moisture from your mushrooms. The process could take between four and eight hours, so set a timer and check your mushrooms every two hours. Once your mushrooms can snap when pressure is applied to them, like a potato chip, they are ready to be stored.

Air Dried

This method is cost-effective, easy to access, and works great if you live in a dry environment. But it isn't foolproof, and I wouldn't recommend it for those who live in humid environments. However, even after the drying process is complete, there is a chance that your mushrooms may still contain some moisture in the middle, therefore I normally use it to give my harvest a few extra days of shelf-life.

Using the same method you used during the pre-drying step, you will now lay your mushrooms down on kitchen paper or a fresh towel in front of a fan, but make sure none of them are touching one another, in an environment with relative humidity below 55%. The room you place the mushrooms in should also be well-ventilated, and the fan needs to be positioned in a way that allows it to blow air over the mushrooms. If you have a heater, a fireplace, and a black or dark towel, put the mushrooms as close to the heating elements while drying for better results. Place new layers of kitchen paper under the mushrooms every day. Continue this method until most of the moisture is drawn out. You will check on them frequently and once they become rigid and snap under pressure, they are ready.

Desiccant

While natural drying is an easy method, it is not the most effective. The ideal scenario is to get your mushrooms "cracker dry," which means they snap easily when you bend them. Buying a dehydrator is the best option, but this can be pricey. A cheaper option is to use a desiccant like silica gel, which you can buy in small packets online or find in cat litter. Follow these step-by-step instructions:

- Leave your mushrooms out to dry for 48 hours. Set up a fan if you have one.

- Put a base layer of the silica packets/cat litter into an airtight container.

- Place a wire screen or rack over the desiccant and arrange the mushrooms onto it. The mushrooms should be elevated enough that they are not touching the desiccant.

- Seal the container and leave it for a couple of days. To test whether the mushrooms are dry, try snapping one in half. Once they become brittle, they are ready to be stored in a fresh, but airtight, container.

- Transfer to glass jars, airtight container, or zipper bag for storage, and keep in a cool, dark place.

I don't recommend drying your mushrooms in the oven because of the lack of ventilation, and putting them in an area with static, hot air will cook them instead of drying them. Some users still do it by leaving the oven door open and lifting them from the bottom, keeping the temperature low. This might work but I have never tried it.

There is no real-time limit to how long it will take to dry your batch. Remember, variables such as environment, equipment used, the size of the bunch, and how big the specimens are, all play a role. Instead, identify specific trademarks, including whether the stem snaps when you break it. Is the cap brittle and does it turn to powder if you continue to break it down? As soon as you've effectively dried them, you'll want to make sure you store the mushrooms correctly.

Storing

Dried mushrooms can last for over a year if stored properly. Your mushrooms must not come into contact with oxygen, heat, and ultraviolet (UV) radiation during storage for effective preservation. I wouldn't recommend cold storing either, nor storing long-term in powder form, as a study aiming to determine the stability of tryptamines found that powdered mushrooms and cold exposure resulted in a decrease in their potency at a faster rate (Theibert, 2021). They should be perfectly fine if you store them at room temperature in an airtight container placed in a dark place.

Capsules

Capsules allow you to measure out the correct amount for microdosing, saving you time. A clever method is to keep your dried mushrooms intact and only turn them into powder form when you prepare a week's dose. The less you fiddle with your dried mushrooms the better. Once your capsules are filled, place them in a container that has a desiccant, just like the tablets in a medicine bottle.

Mason Jars

You can buy mason jars at your local grocery store, just be sure to clean and sterilize them before use. It's probably one of the easier methods to store your mushrooms and allows them to last for up to 12 months in a cool, dry, and dark environment. Write the date of initial storage on your jar so you can keep track of when you first filled it, and ensure the jar is sealed properly.

Ziploc Bags

Just like mason jars, you can buy ziploc bags meant for food storage at your local supermarket. They are easy to access and cost-effective. After placing your mushrooms in the bag, squeeze out all the air from the bag—without crushing your mushrooms—and seal it. Check the bag for any excess air or holes that could allow oxygen and moisture in. Some users will then zip lock the bag and place it in a mason jar to ensure no air or moisture can get in. You will store the bag containing your mushrooms in a cool, dark, and dry area. Additionally, you can add a silica gel packet in the ziplock bag or mason jar, separated from the mushrooms with a piece of paper towel.

Chapter 13: Bonus

Neuroscience: Your Brain on Psilocybin

So what does psilocybin actually do to your brain? Psilocybin is the main active psychedelic compound in magic mushrooms, but it's not the only one. Psilocybin is metabolized by the human body and turned into psilocin, the substance primarily responsible for the effects of magic mushrooms. Psilocin engages the 5HT2A serotonin receptors in your brain. While research is still relatively nascent, studies have confirmed several significant effects that psilocybin has on the brain.

One of these is its direct impact on the brain's neuroplasticity, i.e., the function that enables us to grow and learn, adapt, and change. It helps stimulate neurogenesis—the formation of new brain cells—which in turn forges new neural pathways in the brain. This is especially apparent in the hippocampus, an area of the brain that promotes memory and learning. Some researchers have even gone as far as saying that psilocybin has the potential to "reset" our Default Mode Network (DMN). The DMN is a network of interacting regions in the brain that activate when we are not focused on the outside world or what is happening around us. For example, when we are daydreaming, or completely engrossed in one task. Psilocybin is thus able to rewire old habits, which may explain why treatment has been so effective for people trying to give up smoking and alcohol, as well as tackling other mental health problems like anxiety.

This is closely related to another effect researchers are observing—the ability of psilocybin to promote interconnectivity between cerebral regions that were otherwise compartmentalized. In other words, it connects areas of the brain that don't usually work together. It can build new networks, disrupt others, or "rebuild" old ones that have become structurally unstable. Psilocybin increases the connectivity between specific areas in the brain—for example, those involved in sensation and movement. On the other hand, it decreases connectivity between the areas that are responsible for planning and decision-making.

This means it can break down many parameters that we often use to organize and process, allowing us to think more open-mindedly and forgivingly. Researchers have taken brain scans of this activity and found that the brain on psilocybin is neurologically similar to states achieved through mindfulness, meditation, and dreaming. That should reassure any apprehensive first-time trippers! So now that you have had a glimpse of the neuroscience behind it, it won't come as a surprise to hear of the extraordinary therapeutic potential of psilocybin.

In my other book, *Microdosing Psilocybin Mushrooms: An Essential Guide to Microdosing Magic Mushrooms & Microdosing Journal*, I go into more depth about the effects of psilocybin on our brain and all of its therapeutic applications (some are discussed in the next section). Please refer to that if you wish to learn more about this particular area.

The Therapeutic Potential of Psilocybin

After a 40-year hiatus, research into psilocybin that started in the 1960s is finally starting to pick up again. The breakthrough came in 2006, when John Hopkins University published a study detailing "the safety and enduring positive effects of a single dose of psilocybin," triggering a worldwide revival of psilocybin research. In the year before this book was published, there was more research into psilocybin than ever before in history. Now, as astonishing results continue to be published and psilocybin becomes less stigmatized, more research is being conducted into its therapeutic effects.

For example, in the US, the Food and Drug Administration (FDA) and the Drug Enforcement Agency (DEA) have recently authorized a number of small studies to look into the use of psilocybin in medical and psychiatric contexts. Already they have found that psilocybin has a profound effect on people suffering from migraines, cluster headaches, addiction, anxiety, depression, obsessive-compulsive disorder (OCD), and post-traumatic stress disorder (PTSD), just to mention some of them. For depression in particular, the FDA labeled it "a breakthrough therapy." Not only has a single dose of psilocybin been shown to substantially minimize people's symptoms for a surprisingly long time, but in some extraordinary cases, it has cleared them up completely.

Psilocybin is also being trialed as a way to alleviate chronic pain and psychological distress in patients with terminal cancer. Despite being very new, the results of the therapy are already extremely encouraging, with patients experiencing a significant decrease in levels of depression and end-of-life anxiety and fear.

Even if you do not suffer from poor mental and physical health, there are many reasons to take psilocybin. If you are reading this book, you probably already know that. The biggest reason is for your own personal growth. It can have a hugely positive impact on your brain's capacity and productivity. It can improve your concentration and mood, increase energy levels, and enhance your communication and relational skills. It can also promote creative thinking, self-realization, and a connectedness to the natural world. In fact, many people who have had a high dose of psilocybin have reported intense spiritual experiences that have had a lasting positive effect on their lives. I always try to be as objective as possible in this matter as each individual is different, but I have to say that, from my own experience with this powerful substance, I certainly felt all of these well-being benefits. With such promising results already, one can only imagine how many more extraordinary therapeutic effects we are soon to discover.

Dosage Guide and Microdosing

Every person is unique, and each individual will experience a slightly different journey on mushrooms. Remember, this is something to embrace, not be intimidated by. There are a number of different factors to take into account before starting your mushroom trip. You must be mindful of the setting or environment you are in, the company you are in (if any), your emotional state, the strain of mushroom you have chosen, how you've prepared it, your own personal body weight and chemistry, and your individual sensitivity to the substance. As with everything in life, you must also take the right dose. It is crucial to know what you want out of your trip, and therefore how much you need to take. Making an informed decision at this point is the difference between a wonderful, life-changing experience, and a potentially bad trip.

Please note that all quantities in the below guide refer to *Psilocybe cubensis* mushrooms in their dried form. They are usually weighed this way for better accuracy. If you don't want to eat them in their dried form, you can brew your mushrooms into a tea, blend them with a smoothie, or mix them with a strong-tasting flavor (Nutella being a popular one!) Just bear in mind that how you prepare your mushrooms will affect the onset of your trip. For instance, you will feel the effects faster if you drink your mushrooms as tea rather than physically ingesting them.

Dosage Guide

On average, people will start to feel the effects of psilocybin mushrooms at 0.2–0.5g, although of course, this will vary from person to person. Once you start hitting low to moderate doses, a mushroom trip can be broken down into four main phases: ingestion, onset, peak, and comedown. Predictably, the "peak" phase is when the trip is at its most intense, typically occurring two hours after ingestion. If you know what to expect, you have nothing to fear. Overall, a mushroom trip will typically last between 3–6 hours. Please remember not to take the common effects detailed below as an exhaustive list. It is meant as a helping hand to give you a better idea of what to expect, based on people's past experiences.

Microdose: 0.1–0.3g (it can be up to 0.5g or below 0.1g, depending on the person and needs)

Contains less than 4 mg of psilocybin.

Microdosing is when you take a very small amount of psilocybin mushrooms on a regular basis so as to reap the benefits without experiencing their psychedelic effects. This is also known as taking a sub-perceptual dose. Individuals microdose to enhance their creativity, improve their mood or energy levels, increase focus, or encourage more positive and profound thinking patterns. Microdosing is also commonly used by people who suffer from anxiety, depression, or migraines (among others) as an alternative to prescription medication.

Common effects to expect:

- decreased levels of stress and anxiety

- mood enhancement

- improved communication skills

- stabilized energy levels

- increased motivation and confidence

- increased creativity and ability to think clearly

- enhanced physical stamina and endurance

- possible visual alterations or distortions (you may have hit the low dose range instead of a microdose)

Low Dose: 0.5–1g

Contains approximately 4–10 mg of psilocybin.

Sometimes called a "museum dose," a low dose like this will allow you to feel the effects of psilocybin without significantly altering your sense of reality, i.e., you could visit a museum and still seem relatively normal to other people.

Common effects to expect:

- slight physical high

- mild visuals, such as "breathing" surroundings

- mood enhancement to point of euphoria

- increased confidence and fluidity in conversation

- introspection

- deeper thoughts

- heightened emotional response to your surroundings, including people, music, art, objects, etc.

- enhanced senses; colors are more vibrant

- increased creativity

- distorted sense of time

Moderate Dose: 1–3 g

Contains approximately 8–20 mg of psilocybin.

This is where you start to feel the psychedelic effects. You may start to get visual hallucinations, and things like space, time, texture, and depth may appear distorted. Nevertheless, with a dose like this, you are still relatively grounded in the world around you.

Common effects to expect:

- a more distinct timeline of the trip: feeling the come-up, peaking, and then the comedown

- heightened emotions

- enhanced appreciation of music, art, and even mundane, everyday objects

- laughter

- colors are more vibrant

- increased introspection and deep thinking

- a sense of openness and connection to the world and other people

- feeling deeply relaxed and at peace

- synesthesia

- distorted sense of time

- altered visual perception, including halos of light around people and objects

- closed and open-eye visuals, including fractals and geometric patterns

- compulsive yawning

- difficulty carrying out cognitive and physical tasks

High Dose: 3–5 g

Contains approximately 20–35 mg of psilocybin.

Now you're away! With a dose like this, you will experience the full psychedelic effects of these wonderful little fruits.

Common effects to expect:

- a clear come-up, peak, and comedown

- a feeling of dissociation from your body

- strong closed and open-eye visuals

- dream-state feeling

- hallucinations

- laughter

- intense emotions and feelings of profundity and wonder

- life-changing thoughts and realizations

- a sense of openness and connection to the world and other people

- feeling deeply relaxed and at peace

- synesthesia

- no sense of time, or time becoming meaningless

- difficulty carrying out cognitive and physical tasks

- you might feel the presence of unknown or divine entities

Heroic Dose: 5 g+

Contains over 35 mg of psilocybin.

The clue is in the name. I would only recommend this kind of dose to a seasoned tripper.

Common effects to expect:

- mystical experience

- life-changing thoughts and realizations

- ego death or ego dissolution

- intense emotions and feelings of profundity and wonder

- very strong hallucinations (that you may mistake for reality)

- synesthesia

- no sense of time, or time becoming meaningless

- disorientation

- potential loss of motor neuron functionality

Entering into a psychedelic trip can seem like a terrifying loss of control to some people, but if you factor in all of these variables and use them to establish your own parameters, you will set yourself up for a successful, stress-free trip. It will also lower the chances of you having a so-called "bad trip," but please be aware that it can still happen. Let's look at the risks.

Risks and Disqualified Individuals

First, it should be said that psilocybin is relatively safe, being considered one of the safest recreational drugs in the world. It doesn't contain any processed or added toxins; it's non-addictive, and it is essentially impossible to overdose. Having said that, it is possible to have a bad trip, and as with any mind-altering substance, taking psilocybin mushrooms has its risks. During the come-up, it is possible to experience some physical side effects such as nausea, vomiting, tremors, and numbness. Throughout the trip in general, it is also possible to experience negative hallucinations, paranoia, panic attacks, and, in some rare cases, psychosis.

Possible side effects

The side effects you can experience when you take psilocybin can include but are not limited to

- nausea

- vomiting

- icy chills or facial flushes

- tingling sensations

- upset stomach

- visual alterations or distortions

- frightening hallucinations

- headaches

- impaired concentration

- hyperactivity

- increased temperature

- increased or irregular heart and breathing rate

- high blood pressure

- lack of coordination

- muscle weakness*

- agitation

- insomnia

- drowsiness

- anxiety or nervousness

- confusion

- paranoia

- panic reactions

- dry mouth

- loss of appetite

- sweating

- diarrhoea

- unusual body sensations

- seizures

- psychosis**

* The risk of a rare paralysis (wood lover paralysis) is also present, which seems to come only from mushrooms that grow on wood, hence the name. Symptoms appear hours after ingestion and include weakness, lack of coordination, or even paralysis.

** If you have a personal or family history of psychotic disorders like schizophrenia, are at risk of developing one, or currently have one, you have to be cautious about using psychedelic substances altogether. Additionally, individuals with bipolar disorder are normally excluded from clinical trials due to fears of aggravating their condition or triggering manic episodes.

Currently, no deaths, injuries, or illnesses have been specifically linked to the safe use of mushrooms containing psilocybin.

Psilocybin effects are limited to the timeframe of the trip and do not have long-term repercussions. However, in some rare cases, after taking a psychedelic substance—normally at higher dosages—a person can experience persisting changes in their perception, hallucinations, or episodic flashbacks, all of which would only normally occur during the "trip". This disorder is known as "hallucinogen persisting perception disorder" (HPPD).

Disqualified Individuals

Because we currently don't know the exact effects of psilocybin on a host of medical and mental health disorders, especially in the long-term, you should always proceed with caution and consult with your healthcare provider. In general, **you should avoid microdosing with psilocybin if** you

- are pregnant or breastfeeding

- are taking medications that could trigger a negative interaction, especially antidepressants, Tramadol, or lithium carbonate medicine*

- have psychosis or a family history of psychosis, including schizophrenia

- struggle with paranoia

- have recently ingested alcohol or other drugs

- have bipolar disorder, including a family history

- have heart disease**

- have abnormal liver functions

- experience epilepsy

- have other conditions that have not yet been identified (or specified here) as being triggered by, or interact badly with psilocybin

* In general, you should avoid combining any medications (mood stabilizers, anxiolytic or antipsychotic medication, antidepressants,

psychostimulants, or painkillers), especially if they are psychoactive—like antidepressants, Xanax, and Adderall—as they work on your serotonin system. Psilocybin (active metabolite psilocin) is a serotonin agonist, so when these medications interact with psilocybin, you could experience adverse side effects.

** There are concerns that microdosing with psilocybin could worsen or negatively affect heart conditions. Additionally, there is a theory regarding valvular heart disease (VHD)—which causes weakness, shortness of breath, and sudden cardiac death—that believes medications that have a tendency to bind with the serotonin 2B receptor (5HT2B) may trigger this disease. As psilocybin has an affinity for binding with the 5HT2B receptor, there is concern that it may cause VHD if you microdose with psilocybin in the long term (Thomas, 2022).

You need to be aware of possible issues you could face so that you can sufficiently prepare yourself before deciding whether you want to ingest any dose of psilocybin or not. I would recommend that if you find yourself in any of the disqualifying circumstances mentioned in the book—and even other ones not mentioned here—or suspect you have a predisposition to them, or to any other that can be contraindicated, that you first speak with your medical provider before taking your first dose of psilocybin.

Stopping a Bad Trip

If you do experience negative thoughts or emotions while tripping, the best thing to do is to remain calm and remind yourself that this is a temporary state. Do not resist it, as this will make it worse. Many people have reported an astonishing ability to acknowledge and accept negative thoughts and emotions while tripping. If you look at it less as a threat and more as an opportunity to learn about yourself, you can come away with a deep sense of satisfaction and higher self-awareness.

Unfortunately, we have no "off switch" so once our bad trip starts the only thing we can do is to try and transform it into a more positive experience.

A few ideas to try to potentially help stop a bad trip include:

- Staying away from people and places that might upset you or freak you out.
- Don't take shrooms when you know something is bothering you.
- Avoid locations that may be over-stimulating, such as busy, brightly lit public areas.
- Stay close to people you trust.
- Ultimately, figure out what would make you feel safer or more comfortable. This can include listening to your favorite playlist, dancing, meditating, getting some fresh air, or even hiding under a blanket like when you were a kid.

It's important to remember that you have the ability to turn your trip around. Many shroom users say their "bad trip" benefited them in some way, shape, or form.

Conclusion

Growing mushrooms at home is not just an insightful and rewarding hobby; it can provide you with the tools to embark on a deeply spiritual journey of self-reflection and awareness or allow you to start your own microdosing journey. After reading this guide, you should understand the basics of the fungi life cycle and what you need to replicate it in your own home. The key to success is to keep in mind the four fundamentals: temperature, air exchange, moisture, and light exposure. Knowing when to introduce and adjust these parameters is what elevates the novice into a seasoned cultivator. The other most important thing to remember is contamination. This will be your worst enemy, so sterilize everything every step of the way. If it feels like it's too much, you're probably getting it just right.

We have looked at some of the main mushroom-growing teks in this guide. I would suggest trying a more straightforward one first, and then once you feel more confident, perhaps have a go at setting up your own Martha tent or monotub, or even an outdoor cultivation patch! When sourcing your spores or any other growing equipment, take care to check the reviews and don't be afraid to inquire with the suppliers. Once you've had a successful harvest, remember that it doesn't end there! Refer back to this guide on how to continue the cycle by collecting your own spores and growing with liquid and agar cultures.

I am certain that you will come away from this whole process with a greater appreciation of fungi and their vast underground networks. They truly are the earth's central nervous system. They are intelligent communicators, powerful healers, and the regenerative source of all life. All this we know already, and yet there is still so much left to discover about what fungi are capable of. It is truly my hope that, having read this guide, you will go on to experience the joy and satisfaction of cultivating psilocybin mushrooms and reap the extraordinary therapeutic benefits. Enjoy tapping into this source of wisdom and power that has been supporting and inspiring humans since our earliest existence.

Dear Reader

I want to personally thank you for choosing this book from among dozens out there, for acquiring an authorized copy of it and supporting my work, and for making it all the way to the end.

If you liked the content, please consider posting a review or rating on Amazon, it would mean a lot to me and it would help others benefit from my work. It is also the best way to support independent writers like myself.

You can use your respective Amazon market if you don't live in the UK or US.

Thank you.

Amazon US

Amazon UK

References

Bil Harret. (2022). *Psilocybin Mushrooms*. Inspirational Creator.

David Sanders. (2022, September 17). Image contributor: Growing process and other samples.

90 Second Mycology. (2021, January 18). *Perfect Success With the "Uncle Ben's® Tek" EVERY TIME! \ Show This Video to the HATERS! (Mushrooms)*. Www.youtube.com.

Barlow, C. (2021, October 27). *How to use Agar in Mushroom Cultivation*. DoubleBlind Mag.

Byrne, M. (2014, July 5). *Mushroom Tripping Is a Lot Like Dreaming, Biologically Speaking*. Www.vice.com.

Double Blind Magazine. (2023). *Shrooms*. DoubleBlind Mag.

Ercolano, A. (2021). *Johns Hopkins Center for Psychedelic and Consciousness Research*. Www.hopkinsmedicine.org.

Ginder-Shaw, E. (2019, July 11). *Mushroom Retreats & Research on The Rise: History & Science*. Third Wave.

Griffiths, R. R., Johnson, M. W., Carducci, M. A., Umbricht, A., Richards, W. A., Richards, B. D., Cosimano, M. P., & Klinedinst, M. A. (2016). Psilocybin produces substantial and sustained decreases in depression and anxiety in patients with life-threatening cancer: A randomized double-blind trial. *Journal of Psychopharmacology*, 30(12), 1181–1197.

Harret, B., & Sasha, A. V. (2022). Microdosing Psilocybin Mushrooms: An Essential Guide to Microdosing Magic Mushrooms & Microdosing Journal. In *Amazon*. Inspirational Creator.

Haze, V., & K Mandrake. (2016). *The psilocybin mushroom bible : the definitive guide to growing and using magic mushrooms*. Green Candy Press, P.G.W. China.

How to grow psychedelic mushrooms for the first time. (2022, September 8). Leafly.

Magic Mushrooms Shop. (2021). *Liquid Culture Growth Medium in 5, 10 and 25ml vials | buy online*. Www.magic-Mushrooms-Shop.com.

Magic Spores Shop. (2015). *Spore vial instructions: How to use a magic mushroom spore vial ? / Magic Spores Shop - About cultivation of magic mushrooms*. Www.magic-Spores-Shop.com.

Mushroom Prints. (2022). *Mushroom Spore Syringes and Edible Culture*. Mushroom Prints.

North Spore. (2022, November 11). *How to Make a Martha Tent Mushroom Fruiting Chamber*. North Spore.

North Spore. (2023). *Monotub Tek: How to Make a Monotub and Grow Mushrooms Indoors*. North Spore.

Ordonez, M. A. (2022, January 4). *What Does Blue Bruising Mean On Magic Mushrooms?* Www.zamnesia.com.

OttO. (2006, January 29). *A *beginner friendly* method for making Liquid Culture - Mushroom Cultivation Archive - Shroomery Message Board*. Www.shroomery.org.

Parsons, A. (2021, January 4). *Everything You Need To Know About Magic Mushroom Substrates*. Www.zamnesia.com.

Parsons, A. (2021, August 26). *Creating A Magic Mushroom Outdoor Patch*. Www.zamnesia.com.

Parsons, A. (2022, April 25). *What Is A Magic Mushroom Spore Vial?* Www.zamnesia.com.

Philly Golden Teacher. (2020, October 11). *PGT Agar Cups Recipe (Ez as 123)*. Www.youtube.com.

Philly Golden Teacher. (2020, December 6). *The Agar Files - Spore Print to Agar (Intro to Agar)*. Www.youtube.com.

Philly Golden Teacher. (2020, December 27). *The Agar Files - Making Transfers on Agar*. Www.youtube.com.

Philly Golden Teacher. (2021, January 16). *Inoculating Agar to Grain - The Agar Files*. Www.youtube.com.

Philly Golden Teacher. (2022, January 22). *PGT Mushroom Martha Tent Overview*. Www.youtube.com.

Principium Quaesitor. (2014). *Magic Mushroom Grower's Guide Simple Steps to Bulk Cultivation*. Principium Quaesitor.

Psilocybin Mushrooms. (2023). *r/PsilocybinMushrooms*. Reddit.

Rindskopf, J. (2022, February 9). *10 Things You Should Know Before Buying Psilocybin Spores*. Third Wave.

Ryan. (2023). *Psilocybe Cubensis Mushroom Spore Syringes*. Premium Spores.

Sam. (2021, December 24). *Mushroom Liquid Cultures: How, Why and Where to Buy*. Fungi Academy.

Sargent, M. (2022, April 19). *How To Build A Martha Fruiting Chamber For Mushrooms.* Www.zamnesia.com.

Shaman Mushroom Spores. (2022). *About Our Focus and Mushroom Products*. Shaman Mushroom Spores.

Shroomery - *PF Tek v2*. (2011, June 2). Www.shroomery.org.

Shroomok. (n.d.-a). *How to store Mushroom Spawn for a long time and postpone Spawn to Bulk | Mushrooms Q&A by Shroomok.* Shroomok.com.

Shroomok. (n.d.-b). *Mycology Glossary & Mushroom Growing Abbreviations | Mushrooms Q&A by Shroomok*. Shroomok.com.

Shroomscout. (2020). *r/unclebens - Part 1: How Mushrooms and Mycelium Grow Shroomscout's Comprehensive "Easiest Way to Learn Shroom Growing with Uncle Bens Tek" Instructions*. Reddit.

Shroomscout. (2020). *r/unclebens - Part 2: Inoculating Uncle Bens for Colonization Shroomscout's Comprehensive "Easiest Way to Learn Shroom Growing with Uncle Bens Tek" Instructions*. Reddit.

Shroomscout. (2020). *r/unclebens - Part 3: Spawning to Bulk (Fruiting) Shroomscout's*

Comprehensive *"Easiest Way to Learn Shroom Growing with Uncle Bens Tek" Instructions*. Reddit.

Shroomscout. (2020). r/unclebens - *Part 4: Harvesting, Drying, and Preparing for the Next Flush Shroomscout's Comprehensive "Easiest Way to Learn Shroom Growing with Uncle Bens Tek" Instructions*. Reddit.

SpitballJedi. (2014, June 8). *Agar to Grain (A2G) - Mushroom Cultivation - Shroomery Message Board*. Www.shroomery.org.

SporeAuthority. (n.d.). *SporeAuthority - Trusted Mushroom Spore Site Reviews*. Sporeauthority.com.

Spores Lab. (2022). *Spores Lab | About Us | Canada's Leading Mushroom Genetics Provider*. PNWM.

Sporestock. (2022). *Cubensis Research Spore Syringes*. Spores + Cultures by Spore Stock.

sporetraders. (2020). *r/sporetraders - Vendors List & Buyers Mini-Guide: PLEASE READ!!* Reddit.

Sporevision. (2022). *All*. Sporevision.

Sporeworks. (2023). *Sporeworks.com*. Sporeworks.com.

Stamets, P. (2000). *Growing gourmet & medicinal mushrooms : Shokuyō oyobi yakuyō kinoko no saibai] : a companion guide to The Mushroom cultivator*. Ten Speed Press.

Stamets, P. (2005). *Mycelium running : how mushrooms can help save the world*. Ten Speed Press.

Stamets, P. (2017). *Fungi Perfecti*. Fungi Perfecti.

Sumpter, L. (2022, March 30). *Grow Magic Mushrooms In Bulk Using Monotub Tek*. Www.zamnesia.com.

Sumpter, L. (2022, September 28). *How To Dry Magic Mushrooms - Zamnesia*. Www.zamnesia.com.

Tafra, K. (2021, September 20). *Shrooms Dosage: Chart, Calculator & How-To Guide*. HealingMaps.

The Third Wave. (2018, December 27). *How To Grow Psilocybin Mushrooms At Home*. The Third Wave.

The Third Wave. (2019, January 5). *Everything You Need To Know About Psilocybin Mushrooms (Shrooms)*. The Third Wave.

TheStonedGrower. (2023). *Different types of substrates for mushroom cultivation! 24High*. Www.24high.com.

Wave, T. (2017, January 10). *What To Expect On Your Next Psilocybin Mushroom Trip*. Third Wave.

Zhou, L. (2021, June 11). *Psilocybin Benefits: Magic Mushrooms & Their Many Benefits*. Third Wave.

Image References

Fred JX. (n.d.). *Grow Kit Mycelium*. Shutterstock. Retrieved September 19, 2022, from Shutterstock.

Tishchenko, D. (n.d.). *Mycelium liquid culture. Psilocybe cubensis*. Retrieved December 19, 2022, from Dreamsite.

CannabisPic. (n.d.). *Microcultivo de hongos Psilocybe cubensis*. Retrieved December 19, 2022, from Dreamsite.

Cannabis_Pic. (n.d.-a). El micelio de hongos, stock 1950037318. Retrieved September 19, 2022, from Shutterstock

Made in the USA
Las Vegas, NV
14 February 2024

85810875R00098